SPORTS SCIENCE
A Complete Introduction

Simon Rea

First published in Great Britain in 2015 by John Murray Learning. An Hachette UK company.

British Library Cataloguing in Publication Data: a catalogue record for this title is available from the British Library.

Library of Congress Catalog Card Number: on file.

Paperback ISBN 978 1 47361489 5

eBook ISBN 978 1 47361490 1

2

Cover image © gettyimages.co.uk

Typeset by Cenveo Publisher® Services.

Printed and bound in Great Britain by CPI Group (UK) Ltd., Croydon, CR0 4YY.

John Murray Learning policy is to use papers that are natural, renewable and recyclable products and made from wood grown in sustainable forests. The logging and manufacturing processes are expected to conform to the environmental regulations of the country of origin.

Carmelite House
50 Victoria Embankment
London EC4Y 0DZ
www.hodder.co.uk

Contents

To my incredible wife, Tanya, whose love and support in every decision I have made have made me the happy man I am today. As always, to my parents, Pam and Tony, who helped make this and everything else possible.

Thank you to my colleagues at the Open University, Caroline Heaney, Jessica Pinchbeck, Candice Lingam-Willgoss, Eddie Barker and Rachel Barber-Brock, for their encouragement and support while I was busy writing.

Introduction

Sports science is the application of scientific principles to explain sporting phenomena and provide a basis for improving the performance of teams and individuals. Although human beings have sought ways to gain a competitive edge over their opponents for as long as sports have been played, sports science is a relatively young discipline in the UK and it gained popularity in the last quarter of the 20th century. In the late 1950s and 1960s, the former Soviet Union and Eastern bloc countries applied principles from physics and physiology to sport and successfully improved their performances on the world stage. These developments were matched in the USA in the 1960s. In the UK, sports science became a recognized discipline in the early 1980s when exercise physiologists, biomechanists, sports psychologists, sports nutritionists and professionals from other subjects came together to provide a multidisciplinary approach to analysing and improving sports performance.

In 1984 the British Association of Sport and Exercise Science (BASES) was formed specifically to develop links and communication between those engaged in the scientific study of sport. Also sports science departments, most notably at Loughborough, Leeds and Brighton, started springing up in universities to research and teach degree courses in sports science. There were fewer than 10 universities offering sports science degrees in the 1980s, compared to just under 90 universities that offer the subject today. The provision for sports science boomed in the 1990s as increased opportunities arose to work in sport-related occupations. There was also a huge growth in the number of companies investing in large commercial fitness facilities, such as David Lloyd Leisure and Virgin Active.

At present there are over 200 different types of jobs associated with the sports and fitness industry, with 371,800 people employed within 17,600 businesses (SkillsActive, 2015). In addition there are over 30,000 personal trainers and fitness instructors on the Register of Exercise Professionals (REPs) (SkillsActive, 2015). Sports scientists have come to play a key role for high-performance sports teams, seeking to maximize the performance of these teams and the individuals within them. As well as employing coaches, teams often use sports physiologists, biomechanists, performance analysts, sports nutritionists, sports psychologists and sports massage therapists as they seek to gain any competitive advantage they can.

Key point: Sports science

Sports science is about applying scientific principles to sport and using scientific research to understand sport.

A good example of the power of sports science was the British cycling team under the leadership of Sir Dave Brailsford. As performance director from 2003–14, he put together a team of experts to support the performances of British cyclists for major competitions. He developed a philosophy of 'marginal gains' where nothing was left to chance; this included the quality of the training and nutrition but a lot of attention was paid to ensuring that the cyclists also got the best recovery. He ensured they had advice about adopting the correct sleeping position and having the same pillow to sleep on when they were away from home. The level of attention to detail was impressive and even included bringing in a surgeon to teach cyclists how to wash their hands properly to reduce their chances of becoming ill.

According to the BASES, sports science is principally concerned with three disciplines:

- biomechanics: using mechanical principles to understand human movement and how the human body interacts with equipment and apparatus

- physiology: using biological sciences to investigate how the body responds to exercise and training

- psychology: using psychological principles to provide answers to questions about human behaviour in sports settings.

BASES recommends that sports science should adopt an interdisciplinary approach and should address any performance aspects using two or more disciplines in an integrated fashion (BASES, 2014).

Consequently these three disciplines will form the focus of this book. I have also included a chapter on sports nutrition as it is an area of increasing importance and there are clear links between nutrition and sports physiology. For example, energy production can only be fully understood if we know the form in which energy is introduced into the body. There is also a chapter on planning research in sports science as it is important to understand how the body of knowledge in sports science has been generated.

This book's title is *Sports Science: A Complete Introduction.* The aim is to introduce you to the key research and knowledge in sports science and to provide you with a well-informed starting point in your study of this fascinating subject. Having read the book you will, I hope, be able to discuss sport in a more scientific way and be better able to understand sports performance. Like all other subjects, sports science is continually developing and expanding and the commitment to understanding sport can be a lifelong commitment if you want it to be.

When writing this book I have kept in mind the following quotation, as I believe that deep understanding can only come once the basics of a subject have been grasped.

'Everything should be made as simple as possible but not simpler.'
Albert Einstein (1879–1955), US physicist

While the study of sports science is open to everyone, this book has been written with three main audiences in mind:

- students preparing for study on a university course in sport or sports science; as a student new to the study of sport or sports science you may need to get up to speed quickly on its main principles

- people who are involved in sports and physical activity at all levels who want to understand more about their sports performances and ways in which they can improve their performance

- people who are interested in sport and sports performance and want to learn and understand more about the teams and athletes that they watch.

I have been in all three of these situations and as may be true for you, my own sporting performances sparked my interest in sports science. I competed in track sprinting events from 100 metres to 400 metres and was fascinated at why I could run faster than (nearly) everyone else and why I was so motivated to win races. I had never heard of sports science (it was 1985!)

until my French teacher mentioned that it might be the perfect degree course for me. I knew immediately that sports science was what I wanted to study, and having gained my degree I worked as a lifeguard, fitness instructor, personal trainer and performance coach. After several years I realized that I wanted to be involved in teaching and researching sports science, and have gone on to work in a variety of colleges and universities over the last 20 years.

Where does sports science knowledge come from?

A huge body of knowledge in sports science has been built up owing to the efforts of scientists and researchers. There is another body of 'knowledge' built on anecdotal evidence, where someone has observed something and then come to a conclusion based on this one observation. This 'knowledge' is then passed around and becomes perceived as the 'truth'. This is particularly the case in the field of nutrition, which is full of fallacies and half-truths that have been presented as fact in the media. For example, the relationship between saturated fat in the diet and the prevalence of heart disease has recently been questioned and the research shown to be flawed. However, it provided the basis of our healthy eating guidelines for over 40 years.

When examining knowledge in sports science we need to ask: 'Where is the evidence?' and 'How credible is the evidence?'. The answer must be that the evidence is present in published research. Research will ask questions and then attempt to answer them in a systematic manner. Research is presented in scientific journals, of which there are many dedicated to individual disciplines within sports science. For example:

▶ the Journal of Sport Sciences

▶ the European Journal of Sport Science

▶ the Journal of Sport and Exercise Psychology

▶ the Journal of Strength and Conditioning

▶ the Journal of Sports Medicine.

While a lot of research is picked up by and published in newspapers and magazines, the original articles can be very different. For a start they are written by researchers rather than journalists, who need to present an entertaining or sensational story to their readers. Researchers write journal articles to present their findings to a research community in a transparent way. They present the research question, the method that was used to research the question, the results this method produced, an analysis of the results and the implications that the results have for practice. This is described as primary literature: secondary literature is when these findings are reported in a book, newspaper or magazine.

An article in a specialist journal will have gone through a process of peer review before the journal's editor decides whether it can be published. Peer review involves the journal article being reviewed by other researchers in a similar field as the author. The peer reviewer evaluates the method the researcher used, the sample they chose, the analysis they made and the conclusions that they drew. They make comments and suggestions on how the content of the article could be improved and ultimately recommend whether it should be published or not. To remove any chance of one reviewer being biased, each article is reviewed by a number of peer reviewers.

The peer-review process ensures that only credible research is published and that the published paper is well written and appropriately presented. Once published, each journal article expands the body of scientific literature available to people in that field of practice and the overall knowledge base within a subject.

> 'The greatest obstacle to discovery is not ignorance; it is the illusion of knowledge ...
> I have observed that the world has suffered far less from ignorance than the
> pretensions to knowledge.'
> Daniel Boorstin (1914–2004), US historian

Studying sports science: A multidisciplinary approach

The scope of sports science

As outlined in the introduction, sports science has biomechanics, physiology and psychology as its core subjects. However, over time sports science has come to encompass many other disciplines as well. The scope of sports science covers the subjects shown in Figure 1.1.

Figure 1.1 The scope of sports science

Sports science has been tailored to specific career paths or areas of research interest. For example, many students of sports science are interested in the application of sports science principles to coaching, teaching, fitness training or strength and conditioning development. Hence the inclusion of subjects such as coaching science and strength and conditioning in many sports science programmes.

The sociology of sport looks at the role of sport in society, how sports have developed and why they have become what they are today. For example, in the 19th century and for large parts of the 20th century, higher levels of violence were acceptable in sports; however, as violence has become less acceptable in society, it has become less acceptable in sport as well. Current issues are often examined in the sociology of sport, with social theory being applied to help explain drug use in sport and important social issues such as racism, sexism and homophobia. Once these topics are understood more deeply, action can be taken or policies developed to address these issues.

Motor control is a branch of psychology that examines how motor skills are acquired, coordinated and controlled. Investigations into principles and theories of learning, phases of learning, information processing and the nature of feedback are undertaken in the study of motor control.

Careers in sports science

The growth in sports science courses has been fuelled by the growth in demand for sports science services. This has come from many directions, not least from the need in the UK to offer support services to the many professional and amateur athletes who require advice on every aspect of their performance. Sport has become increasingly professionalized in the UK since receiving the boost of funding from the National Lottery, which has been made available to athletes and for facilities since 1994. Over the 20 years since funding was introduced there has been a disproportionate increase in the success of British athletes in international competitions; Team GB won a total of 15 medals, only one of them a gold medal, at the 1996 Olympic Games, compared with a total of 65 medals, 29 of them gold, at the 2012 Olympics. Home advantage may have played a role in 2012, but it still leads us to question what else happened.

Sports science support has been offered by sport scientists and other graduates working in the following roles:

▶ sports biomechanists

▶ sport psychologists

▶ sports physiologists

▶ performance analysts

▶ sports nutritionists

▶ sports coaches

▶ strength and conditioning coaches

▶ sports physiotherapists and masseurs.

The demand for exercise specialists to advise the general public on their fitness levels and increase their awareness of the benefits of exercise has increased the demand for graduates working in the following roles:

▶ fitness trainers

▶ personal trainers

▶ exercise consultants and advisers

▶ health promotion

▶ sports managers

▶ sports development officers.

The third area in which demand has risen is in the development and distribution of knowledge. There are many graduates working in academic roles as:

▶ sports science lecturers

▶ physical education (PE) teachers

▶ research scientists or associates.

The interest in and development of sport shows no signs of abating. Sports science is able to accommodate students with wide ranges of interest in sport, both academically and practically.

Developing a multidisciplinary approach to sports science

In the introduction, it was mentioned that the British Association of Sport and Exercise Science recommends that an interdisciplinary approach should be adopted to address the performance issues of athletes. This would involve applying knowledge from more than one of the subdisciplines within sports science.

> *'Only connect ... live in fragments no longer.'*
> E.M. Forster (1879–1970), British novelist and critic

To illustrate how a sports scientist or sports science team would adopt an interdisciplinary approach, it is best to look at a case study.

Case study: Henry

Henry is a 21-year-old gymnast who has moved seamlessly from competing successfully at school, club and county level up to national standard. His aim has always been to represent his country at the Olympic Games.

Recently, however, Henry has found that his performances have started to decline and he is performing less well than some of his peers. He has also started to make more mistakes than usual. His response has been to train harder and harder but he has found that this is not producing the results he would like and is leaving him feeling more tired. He has also been talking to other coaches about his performances and where they think he has been going wrong.

Over the past three months he has started to become slightly disillusioned with gymnastics and he finds himself increasingly choosing to get away from gymnastics and socialize with friends away from sport.

Henry decides that he needs to seek help from a sports science support team.

How can sports science professionals help Henry to halt the decline in his performance and start enjoying gymnastics again?

▶ The sports psychology approach

A sport psychologist would look first at Henry's motivation. They would examine how Henry has been motivated over the previous years and how this motivation has changed. It may be that he no longer is as clear about his goals and how to achieve them. Or Henry may be experiencing over-motivation, as his response to failure is to train harder and harder, and this may be having a negative impact on his mental and physical wellbeing.

A sport psychologist may also look at other factors that could be negatively impacting on his performance. Is he experiencing stress either within sport or through external factors, such as his personal life? Or it could be that his over-motivation is causing high arousal levels and increased feelings of anxiety when he is performing? This may explain why he is making more mistakes than usual.

▶ The sports physiology approach

The sports physiologist would look at Henry's physical conditioning and whether his training is producing adaptations that are specific to his performance. For example, is he strong enough and flexible enough for the movements he is performing? Or is this why he is making mistakes? It may be that his aerobic conditioning is not specific enough and the mistakes he is making are the result of fatigue during the performance.

The sports physiologist would also look at Henry's schedule of rest and recovery. They would ask if he was getting appropriate amounts of sleep and rest to ensure he was in optimal condition for competition.

▶ The biomechanics approach

The biomechanist would look at Henry's performance by examining the quality of his movement and the execution of his techniques. They would analyse whether the decrement in his performance and increased prevalence of mistakes was owing to the development of poor techniques. The biomechanist could capture Henry's performances on video and then analyse his movements before giving Henry feedback about any weaknesses and seeking ways to improve these weaknesses.

▶ The nutritionist approach

The nutritionist would analyse whether Henry was eating correctly and getting the correct balance of carbohydrates, proteins, fats, vitamins and minerals to support his training schedule. They would be interested in Henry's body composition and whether it has been changing over the previous few months.

The nutritionist would also be keen to find out what Henry was eating when he was out with his friends and exposed to external influences. They may also question the link between Henry's nutrition and his change in mental approach and attitude, as well as considering whether his mistakes were due to lapses in concentration as a result of not eating correctly pre-competition.

This multidisciplinary approach should cover all bases when analysing where the problems lie with Henry's performance. The more information that can be gained, the greated the probability that any strategies put in place will be effective. The greater the number of perspectives on a problem, the greater the likelihood that it can be solved.

The multidisciplinary approach is also applicable to an individual working with a personal trainer. It is not uncommon for a personal trainer to have three to four sessions a week, each lasting an hour, and their client will expect to see adaptations and fitness gains fairly quickly. If these don't occur, the client will question the effectiveness of the training and the trainer's choice of exercise. However, the issue is probably what the client does the other 165 hours in the week when they are not seeing the personal trainer.

The personal trainer would suggest that to get optimal training gains the client needs to get the appropriate amount of rest and recovery, to support their training with appropriate nutritional strategies and to ensure that they manage their stress levels. It is likely that the client has a busy life, working long hours, and eats when they can rather than taking regular breaks. While a personal trainer mainly applies their knowledge of sports physiology to their interaction with their client, they also need an understanding at least of nutrition and psychology in order to support their client.

Studying for a sports science degree

An online search using 'sports science degree' as a search term will unearth around 60 universities that offer degree courses. Each course has some common ground with the others, but they all also offer unique features. The modules studied will reflect the expertise of the lecturing staff and the facilities that the university offers. Researching sports science degrees is time well-spent, particularly if you know which areas of sports science you are particularly interested in studying.

Generally speaking, degree courses become increasingly specialized as you pass from year 1 into years 2 and 3, but the actual content can differ significantly between universities.

▶ First year study

All first year study is intended to provide a broad basis of knowledge in sports science and acts as a platform for study in future years. It is worth remembering that students enrolling on the first year of a degree are coming from different backgrounds. They may have studied 'A' levels that have some relevance to degree level study or they may have completed a national diploma in sports science. There may be mature students who are looking to change the direction of their career or who have retired from competitive sport and are embarking on the next step in their career.

The aim of the university is to get every student to the same standard of learning by the end of the first year so that they are equally prepared for the advanced level of study in the second and third years. A sound grounding in anatomy and physiology, sports physiology, biomechanics and sports psychology is a minimum requirement for first year study.

Study of these core subjects will probably be accompanied by an introduction to research skills that will assume increasing importance in the later years. First year study also involves working to develop academic skills such as writing in an academic style, referencing sources correctly, structuring work in different ways (scientific reports, essays), selecting and evaluating appropriate sources of information. Many first year degree courses also offer modules that support the development of skills in other modules; for example, mathematics and biochemistry assist in biomechanics and sports physiology respectively, while knowledge of statistics is vital in understanding research journal articles and for conducting your own research.

It is a common complaint that students don't always see the relevance of some of the subjects that they study in the first year. Statistics and mathematics are prime examples of this; however, in the second and third years of study, lecturers will assume that the students have these skills and knowledge. It also becomes clear that any gaps in a student's knowledge will act as barriers to their achievement.

▶ Second year study

It is common practice in universities that a student has to pass all their subjects, exams and coursework, to progress into the second year. The aim of the second year is to extend student knowledge of the core subjects of physiology, psychology and biomechanics, and then to give students the chance to specialize in certain subject areas.

Most second year programmes offer a blend of compulsory modules and optional modules. Optional modules are often designed to extend students' specialist knowledge. For example, rather than studying sports psychology, modules may focus on areas within sports psychology such as 'groups and teams', 'exercise psychology' or 'career transitions'. In sports physiology, modules can focus on subjects such as 'environmental physiology' or 'exercise at altitude'.

The second year programme extends students' knowledge of research skills and offers modules such as 'research design and analysis' or 'research methods and data analysis'. The emphasis here is to develop skills that are essential for third year study.

▶ Third year study

The third year offers the opportunity for increased specialization. There may still be compulsory and optional modules but it is likely the number of compulsory modules will be reduced and the number of optional modules increased. Some universities dispense with compulsory modules completely and the optionality reflects their expectation that students now have the grounding in sports science that they need but will want to concentrate on specific subjects.

The main focus of the third year is the research project or dissertation. This represents the ultimate in specialization, as it sits within one of the subdisciplines of sports science. The dissertation is an independent piece of research which is selected, conducted and written up by each student. A dissertation is 8000–10,000 words in length and represents the most academically demanding piece of work the student will have done up to this point. The student has to select subjects willing to be involved in an experiment, conduct the research appropriately and then analyse and present their findings. There is a very specific structure that must be adhered to when presenting research findings.

Early in the third year, students will be asked to submit a research proposal that outlines the proposed focus of their research, a suggested title, research method and the expected outcomes from the research.

Once the research proposal has been accepted, each student will be allocated a dissertation supervisor. There will be regular meetings between the student and their supervisor and the supervisor will offer feedback and support to the student. It is common practice for each dissertation to be at least double-marked by the student's supervisor and then one other tutor.

The dissertation is usually the last piece of work that is submitted in a degree and represents about six to nine months of hard work and effort. There may be final year exams as well, but these are often completed before the end of the year so that students have time to focus on their dissertation.

Summary

No doubt you are now aware that sports science is a hugely varied and interesting subject. It helps to answer many questions that are posed about sport and develops your understanding of sporting performance.

The aim of this book is to enable you to consider sports performance from many different angles and appreciate that there is rarely one answer to any problem. As with all subjects, it is most useful to develop a multidisciplinary approach to its study; by applying your knowledge of several subdisciplines your understanding is likely to increase.

I hope this book stimulates your interest and curiosity in sport, or inspires you to study the subject further and perhaps even choose to follow a career in sport.

Dig deeper

Online resources

BASES careers

www.bases.org.uk/Careers

Complete University Guide

www.thecompleteuniversityguide.co.uk/careers/sports-science

www.thecompleteuniversityguide.co.uk/league-tables/rankings?s=sports%20science

Sports Coach UK

www.sportscoachuk.org

Top Universities

www.topuniversities.com/courses/sports-related-courses/guide

Books

American Kinesiology Association (eds), *Careers in Sport, Fitness and Exercise* (Champaign, IL: Human Kinetics, 2014).

J. Masters, *Working in Sport*, 3rd edn (Oxford: How To Books, 2012).

J. O'Leary, *The Times Good University Guide 2015* (London: The Times, 2015).

2

Key principles in anatomy and physiology 1: The musculo-skeletal system

Any study of sports science needs to start with the machine that makes sports performance possible – the human body. The human body has been studied endlessly so that we can understand how it works and how it can be fixed when it goes wrong. In order to decide which muscle groups need to be trained for a specific sport or why you have pain in a certain part of your body, you need to have a sound knowledge of anatomy. Athletes have sought to understand as much as they can about the human body so that they can start to find solutions to the problem of improving their performance.

Chapters 2 and 3 will introduce you to the key systems of the human body involved in producing sporting movements, and what happens to these systems during exercise and sports activities. The human body functions through the integrated actions of 11 systems and we will examine the five systems that are key to sporting movement. Before we examine the systems, we will define the key terms of 'anatomy' and 'physiology' and explore how the systems of the body are structured.

Key terms

Anatomy is the study of the structures that make up the human body. We shall be concentrating mainly on gross anatomy, which involves looking at the larger structures of the body, such as the heart, lungs, skeleton and muscles. Microscopic anatomy focuses on the tiny structures of the body, such as atoms, molecules and cells.

Physiology is the study of how the structures of the body function. For example, once we know about the structure of the heart, we can look at how it functions by acting as a pump to supply oxygenated blood to the tissues of the body.

It is common sense to study anatomy and physiology together because structure and function can never be completely separated. For example, bones are structured in different ways to perform different roles: the bones of the skull are flat and hard to protect the brain, while the bones of the legs are long and strong to support weight and produce efficient movement.

Levels of structural organization of the human body

The human body is organized into six different levels , as shown in Figure 2.1.. Each level builds on the previous levels to take us from the individual atoms and molecules up to the organism itself.

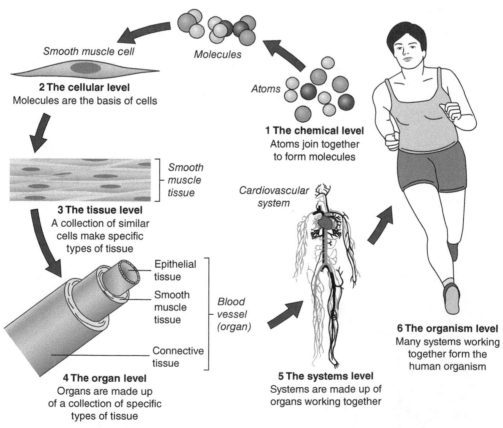

Figure 2.1   The levels of structural organization of the human body

▶ 1 The chemical level

At the simplest level, the human body is made up of atoms, including carbon, hydrogen and oxygen, that combine together to form molecules such as water, sugar and proteins.

▶ 2 The cellular level

Molecules combine to form cells that are the smallest formed units of the human body. There are many different types of cells and they make up over 50,000 different structures in the body. All cells have specific structures in common with each other, such as a nucleus, membrane and DNA, but differ in shape and size to enable them to perform the different functions required of them.

▶ 3 The tissue level

Tissue is a group of cells working together to perform specific functions. For example, groups of muscle cells will make muscle tissue, and groups of brain cells will make brain tissue.

▶ 4 The organ level

Organs consist of large amounts of specific tissue joined together. Organs are recognizable structures of the human body, such as the lungs, heart or stomach, and perform complex functions.

▶ 5 The system levels

Systems are formed by a number of organs working together for a common function. For example, the respiratory system has the lungs as their central organ but it is also dependent on the nose and mouth and a series of tubes, such as the trachea and bronchi, to deliver air to the lungs.

▶ 6 The organism level

When all the systems of the human body combine, we have the organism, or us! Owing to the 11 systems working together, we are able to perform an incredibly wide range of functions from breathing and moving to digesting and assimilating nutrients from food.

'The human body is the only machine in which there are no spare parts.'
Hermann M. Biggs (1859–1923), US physician and public health pioneer

The language of anatomy

When you start to study anatomy and physiology you will realize that it has a language of its own. In particular, you will find that when we describe where parts of the body are in relation to each other, specific terms are used. For example, we may say that the stomach is 'inferior' to the heart, meaning that the stomach lies below the heart physically, rather than that it is less important. When we look at the names of muscles you will come across Latin terms, such as *magnus* and *brevis*, *pectoral* and *deltoid*, which if you have a knowledge of Latin will give you a clue to where they are or what they look like. However, for the beginner to anatomy and physiology they can sound like a foreign language and act as a barrier to understanding the subject. Table 2.1 introduces you to the meanings of some commonly used anatomical terms.

Table 2.1 Commonly used terms to describe position within the body

Term	Definition	Example
Superior	Towards the head or the upper part of a structure	*The lungs are superior to the stomach.*
Inferior	Away from the head or the lower part of a structure	*The intestines are inferior to the stomach.*
Anterior	On the front of the body, or nearer to the front	*The sternum (breastbone) is anterior to the spine.*
Posterior	At the back of the body, or nearer to the back	*The heart is posterior to the sternum.*
Medial	Towards the middle, or midline, of the body	*The sternum is medial to the collarbone.*
Lateral	Towards the outside of the body or away from the midline	*The arm is lateral to the sternum.*
Proximal	Closer to the attachment point of the limb to the body or the midline of the body	*The shoulder is proximal to the elbow.*
Distal	Further away from the attachment point of the limb to the body or the midline of the body	*The ankle is distal to the knee.*
Superficial	On the surface of the body or close to it	*The skin is superficial to the heart.*
Deep	Away from the surface of the body	*The lungs are deep to the ribs.*

In this chapter we will examine three of the body's systems that are important in sports performance: the skeletal system; the muscular system; and the nervous system.

The skeletal system

The human skeleton is an incredible piece of engineering. It is a complex structure with 206 bones forming over 100 joints that offer strength and support as well as flexibility and agility. But it is a bit of a mystery!

▶ How can a structure that is so strong weigh so little? (Bones make up only 8–10 per cent of body weight.)

▶ How can bones be both rigid and flexible?

▶ Are bones actually living tissue?

The secret of bones is that they are hollow structures made of a composite material. In the 20th century, engineers discovered that hollow structures made of composite materials are strongest. Bones consist of calcium, which is a hard mineral, and collagen, which is a flexible protein. If bones were just made of calcium, they would shatter like glass; and if they were just collagen, they would bend like rubber. However, combine the two materials and we have strong, hard bones that are able to bend in response to forces being applied on them. So when we walk or run, the bones can resist the force by bending slightly. Bone is not solid, despite its hard outer shell, as it is made up of interconnecting arches with the appearance of honeycomb. This makes bones light but it also enables them to house blood vessels and nerves. Within the bones an incredible amount of activity occurs as microscopic life forms work tirelessly to maintain the health of the bone tissue. Each week we replace around 5–7 per cent of our bone mass (Hamill and Knutzen, 2009) to ensure that our skeleton never ages.

FUNCTIONS OF THE SKELETON

The skeleton has three main functions to perform.

▶ Support

The skeleton provides structural support and can maintain posture while it is exposed to external forces, such as gravity and ground reaction forces (Hamill and Knutzen, 2009). The bones of the body are smaller at the top of the body in comparison to those at the bottom, in response to the amount of weight that they have to bear. While the upper and lower limbs are similar in structure as they are both made up of three long, thin bones and a joint, the bones of the lower limbs are significantly thicker.

▶ Attachment sites

Bones have specific notches, borders, holes and protrusions to provide attachment points for muscles, tendons and ligaments. A good example of this is the scapula, which is designed to offer attachments for 18 different muscles. The attachment sites act as anchors for the muscles that contract to move bones through joints.

▶ Levers for movement

The long bones of the skeleton act as levers to generate movement. A lever magnifies the force or speed of movement of a bone. When a muscle contracts, it pulls on a bone and together they work to produce movement.

The skeleton performs other functions that are not related to the production of movement. It acts to protect delicate internal organs; for example, the ribcage protects the heart and lungs and the skull protects the brain. The skeleton also provides space for the storage of fats and minerals in the yellow bone marrow. Finally, the production of blood cells, called haematopoiesis, takes place within the hollow structures of the bones.

Key point: Functions of the skeleton

The functions of the skeleton are to provide support, sites for muscle attachment and levers for movement.

MAJOR BONES AND JOINTS OF THE BODY

The mature adult skeleton consists of 206 bones, while a baby's skeleton consists of around 300 bones. During childhood some of the bones fuse together to form single bones. Figure 2.2 shows the major bones of the adult body.

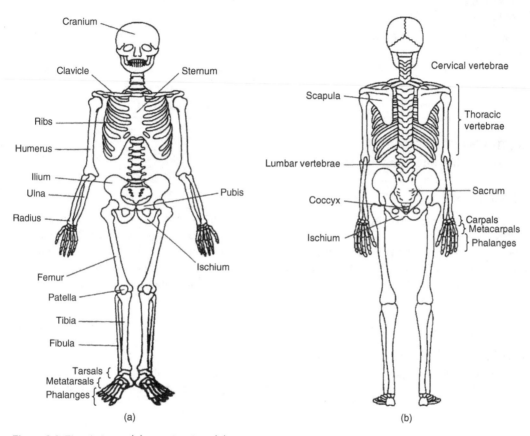

Figure 2.2 The skeleton: (a) anterior view, (b) posterior view

The skull consists of 29 bones, of which there are eight cranial bones, 13 facial bones, six ear ossicles and the hyoid bone, which is situated below the jaw at the top of the neck. The skull is connected to the vertebrae, which has four regions: the cervical (neck), thoracic (chest), lumbar (lower back) and sacroiliac (back of the pelvis). There are 33 vertebrae in total, connected through intervertebral joints. The chest consists of 12 pairs of ribs that are attached (directly and indirectly through cartilage) to the sternum.

The sternum also attaches to the clavicle at the sterno-clavicular joint. The clavicle forms the shoulder joint along with the scapula. They provide a shallow socket for the head of the humerus to fit into at the gleno-humeral joint. The humerus attaches to the ulna and the radius, which is connected to the carpal joints that make up the wrist. The wrist consists of eight carpal bones and the hand is made up of five metacarpal bones. Each metacarpal forms a joint with the phalanges that make up the fingers. There are 14 phalanges in total, five in each finger and two in the thumb.

The lower limb is made up of the pelvis, upper and lower legs and the feet. The pelvis is made up of the fusion of three bones: the ilium, ischium and pubis. The pelvis is connected to the upper leg by the hip joint. The hip joint has a deep socket for the head of the femur to fit into. At the knee joint, the femur forms joints with the tibia (femorotibial joint) and the patella (femoropatellar joint). The lower leg consists of the larger tibia bone and the smaller fibula bone that form joints at the ankle with the tarsals, the seven large bones of the heel. The foot has five metatarsals, which lead to 14 phalanges to make up the toes. Each toe has three phalanges except for the big toe, which has only two.

The skeleton is divided in two distinct parts: the axial and appendicular skeletons (Table 2.2). The axial skeleton provides the central framework of the body and the appendicular skeleton is composed of bones that are hanging from this central framework. There are 80 bones in the axial skeleton and 126 in the appendicular skeleton.

Spotlight: The axial and appendicular skeletons

The axial skeleton is the central part of the bony framework consisting of the skull, vertebrae, ribs and sternum. The appendicular is the parts hanging from the axial skeleton consisting of the shoulder girdle, pelvic girdle, upper and lower limbs.

Table 2.2   The bones of the axial and appendicular skeleton

Structure	No. of bones
Axial	
Cranium	8
Facial bones	14
Hyoid	1
Ear ossicles	6
Vertebrae	26
Sternum	1
Ribs	24 (2 pairs of 12)
Total bones in axial skeleton	**80**
Appendicular	
Clavicle	2
Scapula	2
Humerus	2
Ulna	2
Radius	2
Carpals	16
Metacarpals	10
Phalanges	28
Pelvis	2
Femur	2
Patella	2
Tibia	2
Fibula	2
Tarsals	14
Metatarsals	10
Phalanges	28
Total bones in appendicular skeleton	**126**

THE SPINE

The spine, or vertebral column, is worthy of its own section owing to its importance to the body and its high risk of injury. The vertebral column is shown in Figure 2.3, where you can see its curves.

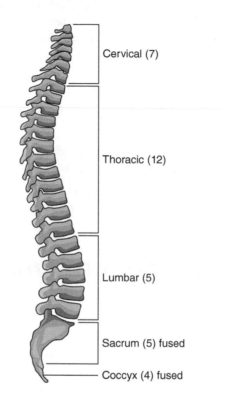

Cervical (7)

Thoracic (12)

Lumbar (5)

Sacrum (5) fused

Coccyx (4) fused

Figure 2.3 The vertebral column

If viewed from the front the vertebral column appears to be straight, but when it is viewed from the side it can be seen to have four slight curves. The vertebral column consists of 33 small bones of irregular shapes, with discs in between each vertebra in the column and ligaments that help to hold the discs in their correct alignment. The vertebral column has five distinct areas, each with differing numbers of vertebrae:

▶ seven cervical vertebrae

▶ 12 thoracic vertebrae

▶ five lumbar vertebrae

▶ five sacral vertebrae (fused)

▶ four coccygeal vertebrae (fused).

In the adult skeleton the five sacral vertebrae are fused to form one triangular bone, called the sacrum, and the final four coccygeal vertebrae form another single triangular bone, called the coccyx. These bones provide a firm foundation for the weight of the upper body. The joints between the other 24 vertebrae offer differing amounts of movement depending upon their position in the column.

The vertebral column has several functions: it must bear the weight of the structures above it; absorb the shocks from forces acting on it (gravity from above and ground reaction forces from below); and offer movements, such as bending forwards, bending backwards and rotating. The structure of each vertebra is specific to its function and the vertebrae at the top of the column are thinner while the vertebrae at the bottom of the column are thicker. On average, cervical vertebrae have a thickness of 3 mm, thoracic vertebrae a thickness of 6 mm and lumbar vertebrae a thickness of 9 mm. However, cervical vertebrae sacrifice strength for mobility while the lumbar vertebrae sacrifice mobility for the strength their thickness provides. This suits them well as the lumbar vertebrae are predominantly weight-bearing while the cervical vertebrae provide the upper body with a wide range of movements.

Spotlight: Why is the spine curved?

The spine has four curves that help to dissipate the forces that are applied to the body. If it was a straight column, these forces would not be cushioned as effectively and the intervertebral discs could become damaged.

The spine has to withstand the force of gravity from above and ground reaction forces from below. These ground forces are increased during running and jumping. The spine has intervertebral discs to assist with shock absorption and they contain a gel-like fluid within its fibrous body. If excess pressure is placed on a disc it becomes ruptured and the fluid can leak out. This leakage can cause pressure on the spinal cord, leading to intense back pain. It is referred to as a prolapsed intervertebral disc but is more commonly known as a slipped disc.

In particular the intervertebral discs are susceptible to damage during compound movements, which is when two movements are combined, such as bending forwards and then twisting.

CLASSIFICATION OF BONES AND JOINTS

Bones are classified according their shape into one of four types: long, short, flat and irregular.

- ▶ Long bones are longer than they are wide, e.g. the humerus and femur.

- ▶ Short bones are generally cube-shaped, e.g. the carpals in the wrist and the tarsals in the heel.

- ▶ Flat bones are usually flat and thin with a large surface area for muscle attachments, e.g. the sternum, ribs and cranium.

- ▶ Irregular bones come in irregular shapes and sizes that cannot be easily described, e.g. all the vertebrae.

Some authors give a fifth type of bone for sesamoid bones, such as the patella, but most place it in the short bone category. Some bones are not easily categorized; for example, the scapula is sometimes categorized as a flat bone and sometimes as an irregular bone.

JOINTS

Joints are also referred to as articulations and are defined as a place where two or more bones meet. These joints are classified in three categories according to the amount of movement they have.

- ▶ Fixed, or fibrous joints have become fused and thus allow no movement, e.g. the bones of the cranium and the three bones of the pelvis.

- Cartilaginous joints have a limited degree of movement as they are held in place by cartilage, e.g. vertebrae are held in place by the cartilage of the intervertebral discs.
- Synovial joints are freely moveable as there is a space between the two ends of bone that are moving, e.g. the knee and the shoulder.

Synovial joints are of most interest to anyone studying sport as they are involved in the movement of the human body. The joint capsule is an important feature of synovial joints as it ensures that two hard ends of bone do not rub against each other. The bones have cartilage at their ends and the capsule provides fluid for lubricating the joint, and ligaments surround it to provide stability. There are six types of synovial joint present in the body:

- Ball and socket joints are made up of a round bone end fitting into a concave rounded socket. These joints provide multiaxial movements (movement in all three planes), as seen at the hip and shoulder joints.

- Hinge joints only allow movement in one plane, just as the hinges on a door only allow it to open and close. The knee and elbow are examples of hinge joints.

- Pivot joints are uniaxial (movement in one plane) as they only allow for movement around a central axis. For example, the joint between the base of the skull and the first cervical vertebra allows us to move our head from side to side.

- Gliding joints consist of two flat surfaces that slide across each other. For example, the tarsal bones in the heel move slightly as the foot pronates and supinates (rolls inwards and outwards).

- Condyloid joints are biaxial as they move in two planes. For example, the wrist can move from side to side as well as backwards and forwards.

- Saddle joints are multiaxial joints that are specific to the thumb joint. It offers humans the skill of manual dexterity as the thumb moves backwards and forwards, from side to side and across the palm of the hand. It enables us to perform complex skills such as holding a teacup or a golf club.

 Key point: Types of joint

There are three types of joint in the body – fixed, cartilaginous and synovial. Synovial joints offer movement and are arranged into six types: ball and socket, hinge, pivot, gliding, condyloid and saddle joints.

▶ The anatomical language of joint movements

Specific terminology is used to describe joint movements. The human body can move in all dimensions or planes and thus we need to be specific when explaining movements. This language ensures that when two professional people are discussing movement, each knows exactly what the other means.

Table 2.3 Commonly used terms to describe joint movements

Term	Definition
General movements	
Flexion	Decrease in the angle of the joint between two bones, e.g. bending the elbow
Extension	Increase in the angle of the joint between two bones, e.g. straightening the elbow
Abduction	Movement away from the midline of the body, e.g. raising the arm to the side of the body
Adduction	Movement towards the midline of the body, e.g. bringing the arm down the side of the body
Rotation	Moving a limb around its central axis, e.g. turning the hand over and back again involves rotation at the elbow
Circumduction	Describing a circular movement of a joint, e.g. drawing a big circle with your hand involves circumduction of the shoulder
Specific movements	
Elevation	Upwards movement of the shoulders, e.g. when you shrug your shoulders
Depression	Downwards movement of the shoulders, e.g. pulling shoulders downwards
Protraction	Pushing the shoulders forwards
Retraction	Pulling the shoulders backwards
Pronation	Movement of the forearm so that the palm of the hand is facing down
Supination	Movement of the forearm so that the palm of the hand is facing upwards
Plantarflexion	Pushing the sole of the foot downwards, e.g. standing on your toes
Dorsiflexion	Pulling the foot upwards towards your shin, e.g. stretching your calf
Inversion	Turning the soles of the feet inwards
Eversion	Turning the soles of the feet outwards

The skeletal system is a complex structure of bones and joints that perform a variety of functions. It is instrumental in giving the body shape, producing movement and protecting organs. It manages to combine strength with lightness and is constantly rebuilding itself. The skeleton can respond to the forces placed on it by reshaping itself to adapt to what is required of it. It provides the strong platform for the rest of the body to build itself around.

The muscular and nervous systems

Muscles produce forces that are the major cause of human movement. They are responsible for allowing us to walk, run, jump, stand upright and resist any forces placed on the body. For these reasons it is important to understand how muscles function and the features that allow these functions to occur. The muscular system is presented here with the nervous system as they are intimately related. Indeed, the muscular system cannot function without activation from nerves. Nervous impulses are transmitted to the muscles, which are highly sensitive, and the muscles respond by producing a contraction.

There are three types of muscle found in the body:

▶ skeletal muscle, which is attached to the skeleton

▶ cardiac muscle, which is specific to the heart muscle

▶ smooth muscle, which is found in blood vessels and the intestines.

Cardiac and smooth muscle are under the control of the autonomic nervous system and thus are involuntary in action: that is, we have no control over when they contract. This is in contrast to skeletal muscle, which is under direct voluntary control. Because of its importance in producing movement, skeletal muscle is the primary focus of this chapter.

Muscle tissue accounts for 40–50 per cent of an individual's body weight (Tortora and Derrickson, 2007), although this figure is largely dependent on how well developed the muscular system is and how much body fat an individual is storing. Body fat can account for 10–30 per cent of body weight. Muscle tissue is predominantly made up of water (70 per cent and protein (23 per cent), and also contains mineral salts (7 per cent).

FUNCTIONS OF SKELETAL MUSCLE

▶ Producing movement

Human movement is a complex process. It is the result of chemical reactions occurring to produce energy that is used to fuel muscular contractions. Muscles are attached to bones via tendons, and muscular contractions produce forces that pull on bones to move them around an axis (the joints), thus enabling the body to produce movement.

Movement of the body – which includes whole body movements such as walking and running and localized movements such as holding a pen or lifting a mug – is a major function of the muscular system.

▶ Stabilizing body position and maintaining posture

Skeletal muscle contractions help to stabilize joints and keep them in the correct position. Skeletal muscle also contracts to keep the whole body in a stable position, i.e. to maintain its posture. Certain muscles, such as those found in the legs and back, have the specific function of holding the body upright against the force of gravity acting down on it.

▶ Producing heat

All muscular contractions produce heat, owing to the chemical reactions taking place to generate energy within the muscles. Muscles can also raise body temperature through shivering if the body falls below a certain temperature. Shivering is actually a series of muscle contractions that produce heat and is part of the body's means of maintaining a consistent body temperature (thermoregulation).

Skeletal muscle also functions as a protective barrier for internal organs, particular those organs of the digestive system that are protected by a wall of abdominal muscle. It also contributes to the passage of food into and out of the body by being responsible for swallowing and defecation.

Key point: Functions of the muscular system

The muscular system is responsible for producing movement, stabilizing the body and holding its posture and producing heat.

MAJOR MUSCLES OF THE BODY

There are around 650 muscles in the human body, so it is unrealistic to expect you to be able to identify all of them. However, a knowledge of the names of 25–30 muscles is crucial for any sports scientist so that they can understand how sporting movements are being produced. It is also important to know how these muscles contract and which sporting movements they are responsible for. The main muscles of the body are shown in Figure 2.4.

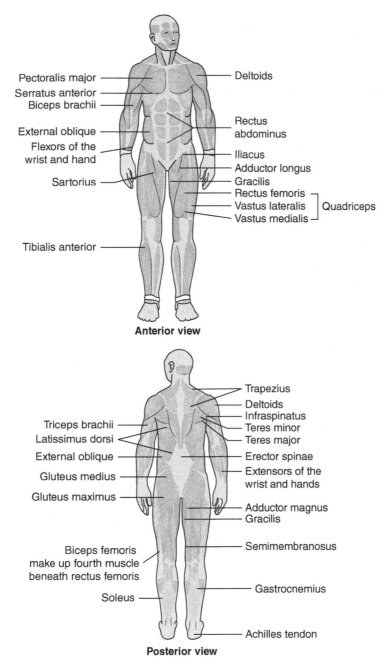

Pectoralis major

Serratus anterior

Biceps brachii

External oblique

Flexors of the
wrist and hand

Sartorius

Tibialis anterior

Deltoids

Rectus
abdominus

Iliacus

Adductor longus

Gracilis

Rectus femoris

Vastus lateralis   Quadriceps

Vastus medialis

Anterior view

Triceps brachii

Latissimus dorsi

External oblique

Gluteus medius

Gluteus maximus

Biceps femoris
make up fourth muscle
beneath rectus femoris

Soleus

Trapezius

Deltoids

Infraspinatus

Teres minor

Teres major

Erector spinae

Extensors of the
wrist and hands

Adductor magnus

Gracilis

Semimembranosus

Gastrocnemius

Achilles tendon

Posterior view

Figure 2.4 The main muscles of the body

▶ Muscles of the upper body

The major muscles of the upper body are the *pectoralis major*, which covers the chest, and the *latissimus dorsi*, which covers the majority of the back. Other important muscles include the *deltoids*, which are the shoulder muscles, the *trapezius*, which runs from the upper vertebrae to the shoulder, the *biceps brachii* at the front of the upper arm and the *triceps brachii* at the back of the upper arm.

▶ Muscles of the trunk and spine

The major muscles of the trunk are the *rectus abdominis* that covers the stomach and the internal and external *obliques* that cover the sides of the stomach. The main muscles of the back are the *erector spinae*, which is a group of small muscles running up and down and across the vertebrae to maintain its upright position. These muscles create the outer layer or outer unit of the trunk and are predominantly responsible for the movements of the spine, such as its rotation, flexion and extension.

There are important muscles lying behind this outer layer which create the inner unit. For example, the *transverse abdominis* behind the *rectus abdominis* and the *multifidus* that assists the erector spinae. The pelvic floor muscles, which run across the pelvis, create the strong muscular base to support and bear the weight of the organs above. This inner unit is vital in stabilizing the vertebrae and the sacroiliac joint (between the sacrum and the pelvis) and preventing injury and any resulting pain.

▶ Muscles of the lower body

The lower body consists of some large groups of muscles. At the front of the thigh are the *quadriceps* muscle, which consists of four individual muscles (*rectus femoris*, *vastus medialis*, *vastus intermedius* and *vastus lateralis*) and the *sartorius*. At the back, the hamstrings muscle is made up of three muscles (the *biceps femoris*, *semimembranosus* and the *semitendinosus*). The adductor muscles (*adductor magnus*, *adductor longus* and *adductor brevis*) make up the inner thigh. In the lower leg the *gastrocnemius* and *soleus* make up the calf muscle and the *tibialis anterior* is the muscle running down the front of the shin.

The muscle fibres which make up each skeletal muscle are composed of thousands of muscle cells. Muscle fibres can be very long, up to 30 cm in length depending on their location. All muscle fibres are surrounded by connective tissue and are connected to blood vessels and nerves. Figure 2.5 shows the gross structure of skeletal muscle, that is, the stages of the muscle from its attachment to the bone via the tendon down to the individual muscle fibre.

Spotlight: Why learning Latin helps you to understand anatomy

The names of muscles are either Latin words or derived from Latin words. Muscles are named in four ways – for their size, shape, position and the direction the fibres run. For example, *pectus* is Latin for 'chest' and *pectoralis* means 'of the chest'. *Major* means 'large' so *pectoralis major* is 'large muscle of the chest'. *Dorsum* means 'back' in Latin and *latissimus* means 'widest' or 'broadest', so the *latissimus dorsi* is the 'widest muscle of the back'. These names describe both position and size and make the muscles easy to locate.

Deltoid means 'triangular', while a trapezius has four sides, describing the shapes of these muscles perfectly. *Biceps* means 'two heads', signifying that the biceps muscle has its origin at two points; similarly, *triceps* has three heads and *quadriceps* four heads.

A muscle with *rectus* at the start of its name will have muscle fibres that run up and down the body, such as the *rectus abdominis*. A *transverse* muscle has fibres running across the body and an *oblique* muscle has fibres running at an angle.

Latin may be regarded as a dead language but if you are involved in sports science or any medical activities, Latin is still very much alive and its knowledge will help you every day.

ACTIONS OF THE MUSCLES

While muscles work together to produce movement, each muscle is responsible for a primary movement. Table 2.4 summarizes the actions that each muscle is responsible for. The table of general and specific joint movements (Table 2.3) will help you to identify what each action means.

Table 2.4 Actions of muscles

Muscle	Location	Joint moved	Action	Example
Pectoralis major	Chest	Shoulder	Horizontal flexion	Bench press
Latissimus dorsi	Back	Shoulder	Adduction	Lateral pulldown
Deltoids	Shoulder	Shoulder	Abduction	Shoulder press
Trapezius	Upper back	Shoulder girdle	Retraction	Bent over row
Biceps brachii	Front of upper arm	Elbow	Flexion	Biceps curl
Triceps brachii	Back of upper arm	Elbow	Extension	Triceps extension
Rectus abdominis	Front of abdomen	Vertebrae	Flexion	Sit up
Erector spinae	Up and down spine	Vertebrae	Extension	Back raise
Gluteus maximus	Back of pelvis	Hip	Extension	Squat
Quadriceps	Front of upper leg	Knee	Extension	Leg extension
Hamstrings	Back of upper leg	Knee	Flexion	Leg flexion
Gastrocnemius	Back of lower leg	Ankle	Plantarflexion	Calf raise
Soleus	Back of lower leg	Ankle	Plantarflexion	Calf raise
Tibialis anterior	Front of lower leg	Ankle	Dorsiflexion	Walking

SKELETAL MUSCLE STRUCTURE

Figure 2.5 shows that the muscle is made up of individual muscle fibres, which are each individually wrapped in the endomysium, a type of connective tissue. Muscle fibres are packaged together into bundles of around 15–20 fibres which are wrapped in another connective tissue, the perimysium. This bundle of 15–20 muscle fibres is called a fasciculus. These fasciculae make up the muscle belly and are themselves surrounded by a third type of connective tissue called the epimysium. The epimysium coats the entire muscle like a sheath and merges into fascia and the tendon that attaches the muscle to the bone it is going to articulate.

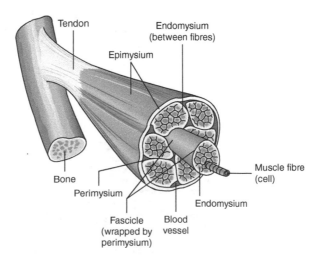

Figure 2.5 The gross structure of muscle fibre

Muscles have a blood supply that delivers oxygen and nutrients; the nutrients are carried and stored in a fluid called sarcoplasm. The muscle fibres are bathed in this fluid, which contains fats and glucose to produce energy, and proteins and enzymes to enable chemical reactions to occur.

▶ Microstructure of skeletal muscle

If we looked at an individual muscle fibre, as seen in Figure 2.5, under a microscope, we would see that it is made up tiny myofibrils. Figure 2.6 shows the individual myofibrils that make up a muscle fibre.

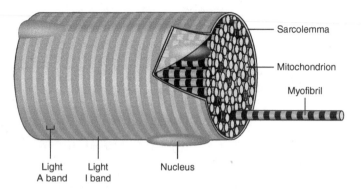

Figure 2.6 Myofibrils within a muscle fibre

There are hundreds of myofibrils in each muscle fibre, each of which are about 1 mm thick (Nedergard, 2015). Myofibrils are surrounded by the sarcolemma, which is a coating around the outside of the muscle fibre where the nerve connects. Mitochondria, which are energy-producing organelles, are interspersed between myofibrils and provide sites for fats and glucose to produce the energy needed for muscular contractions.

Each myofibril contains contractile units called sarcomeres. A sarcomere is described as the functioning unit of the cell, as this is where the muscular contraction occurs. Sarcomeres are lined up adjacent to each other down the full length of the myofibril. Each sarcomere contains thick and thin protein filaments that give skeletal muscle its striped appearance. The sarcomere and its thick and thin filaments can be seen in Figure 2.7. A muscle contraction involves these two filaments sliding across each other.

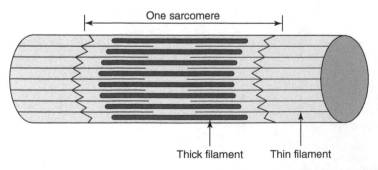

Figure 2.7 A sarcomere, showing its thick and thin filaments

▶ Actin and myosin

The thick filaments are composed of a contractile protein, myosin, and the thin filaments of a second contractile protein, actin. Actin is anchored to each end of the sarcomere at the z-disc. When the muscle contracts myosin binds to the actin, sliding itself, or more accurately pulling itself, along the actin filament. Due to the anchors of the actin on the ends of the sarcomere, the two ends of the sarcomere are drawn towards each other. This shortens the length of the muscle, and we know that when a muscle contracts it becomes shorter. This process can be seen in Figure 2.8. Myosin filaments have projections from their sides, which are called cross bridges, and these provide the attachment to the actin filaments. Once the attachment is made, the cross bridges exert a force on the actin filaments and cause them to move. This is action is known as the sliding filament model.

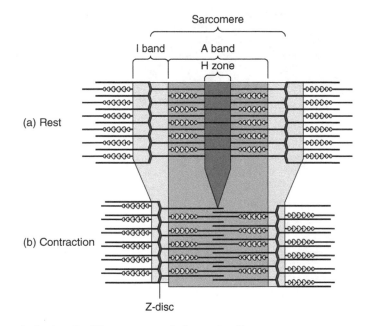

Figure 2.8 Change in the length of the sarcomere during contraction

▶ Troponin and tropomyosin

The binding of actin and myosin is dependent on the actions of two more proteins: troponin and tropomyosin. They are present on the actin filament and can be seen in Figure 2.9.

Troponin is the protein that makes up the myosin binding site on the actin. It is like a hollow cavity but when a muscle is relaxed, its entrance is blocked by a second protein, tropomyosin, which prevents actin and myosin from binding. However, a nervous impulse will cause calcium ions to be released into the sarcomere and the calcium ions act to push tropomyosin out of the way of the binding site and this activates the site. This allows actin and myosin to bind. The myosin then acts by pulling the two ends of the actin together and the muscle contracts. This action is called the power stroke.

MUSCLE FIBRE TYPES

All muscle fibres are attached to a nerve, also called a neurone, that provides an electrical impulse to innervate it and produce a muscle contraction. Each nerve has many muscle fibres attached to it in the form of a motor unit, as can be seen in Figure 2.10.

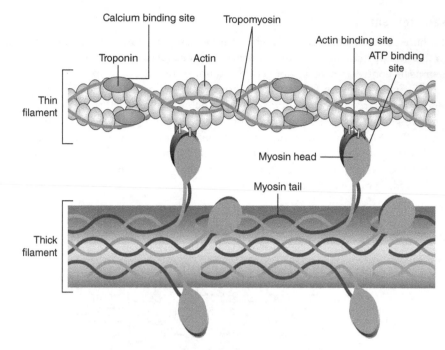

Figure 2.9 Troponin and tropomyosin on the actin filament

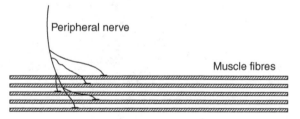

Figure 2.10 A motor unit

Key point: Motor units

A motor unit consists of a nerve and the muscle fibres attached to it.

In Figure 2.9 the nerve to muscle fibre ratio is 1:5 but this is much lower than usual. Most motor units consist of a nerve attached to about 100 muscle fibres, although the number attached depends upon the function of the muscle. The more finely skilled movements are controlled by motor units where the nerve has very small numbers of muscle fibres attached, and motor units performing gross, unskilled movements, such as standing up and sitting down, have large numbers of muscle fibres attached to its nerve.

For example, the quadriceps muscles at the front of the thigh have a nerve to muscle fibre ratio of about 1:400 and the gluteus maximus (buttocks) have a ratio of around 1:1000. The functions of these muscles are predominantly to produce power for movements and to maintain posture. However, muscles in the face which produce fine, delicate movements have a much lower ratio of nerve to muscle fibre. For example, the muscles that move the eyeballs and the tongue have a ratio of lower than 1:10 to provide the fine control of movement that they require.

When a nerve is innervated all the muscle fibres attached to that nerve will contract fully. This is called 'the all or none law'.

Key point: The all or none law

The all or none law states that if a motor unit is recruited, all the muscle fibres attached to that nerve will contract fully or not at all.

When we lift a heavy weight we have to recruit a large number of motor units to enable us to produce enough force to move that weight. In contrast, if we pick up a lighter object, such as a water bottle, we recruit far fewer motor units. The brain will employ its senses to unconsciously make a decision as to how many motor units are required to move a load. The brain is nearly always correct in its assessment of how many motor units are needed. Occasionally it may recruit too few motor units before making a reassessment of the load and then recruiting the correct amount.

SLOW AND FAST TWITCH MUSCLE FIBRES

Every muscle consists of different fibre types called slow twitch and fast twitch fibres. Slow twitch muscle fibres, also called type I, contract slowly and are fatigue-resistant. They are recruited to perform endurance tasks, which involve contracting with low force over a long period of time. To enable them to work over long periods, they need to have a good blood supply so they can be provided with oxygen. As a result they contain many blood vessels as well as a red-coloured protein, myoglobin, which enables them to attract oxygen into the muscles. The red colour of slow twitch muscle fibres is one of their key features. Slow twitch muscle fibres gain their energy for contraction from the breakdown of glucose and fats in the presence of oxygen. This means that they are aerobic and thus capable of prolonged contractions.

By contrast, fast twitch muscle fibres, also called type II, are twice the size of slow twitch muscles and contract, or twitch, at twice their speed, producing contractions of greater force. Fast twitch muscle fibres fatigue relatively quickly and are recruited to perform speed- and power-based tasks. They have a poor blood supply and gain their energy anaerobically through the breakdown of glucose and creatine phosphate that are stored within muscles in small quantities. Due to their relative lack of blood, blood vessels and myoglobin, fast twitch muscle fibres are whitish or grey in colour.

Key point: Slow and fast twitch muscle fibres

Slow twitch muscle fibres are red in colour, have a good blood supply and are slow to fatigue. They are used for endurance activities, such as long-distance running and cycling.

Fast twitch muscle fibres are whitish in colour, have a poor blood supply and fatigue quickly. They are used for speed and power activities, such as sprinting and jumping.

In the human body, postural muscles, such as the muscles found in the legs, core and back muscles are slow twitch, producing low forces over long periods of time and enabling us to stand for prolonged periods of time. The upper body in humans tends to have a greater number of fast twitch fibres. Muscles actually contain a mixture of fast twitch and slow twitch fibres, which can be activated depending upon the body's needs at that time. Humans are designed to have good levels of endurance and speed. The average human has about 50 per cent of each type of muscle fibre in their body, but endurance athletes will have slightly more slow twitch fibres, and speed athletes will have slightly more fast twitch fibres. Table 2.5 shows the relative amounts of fast and slow twitch muscle fibres typically found in specific muscles of the human body.

Table 2.5   Relative amounts of slow and fast twitch fibres in selected muscles (Johnson et al., 1973)

Muscle	% type I fibres	% type II fibres
Deltoid	57	43
Trapezius	54	46
Latissimus dorsi	51	49
Triceps brachii	33	67
Biceps brachii	47	53
Rectus abdominis	46	54
Adductor	59	41
Biceps femoris (hamstrings)	67	33
Rectus femoris (quadriceps)	35	65
Gastrocnemius	51	49
Soleus	88	12

Spotlight: Why is beef red and chicken white?

Before answering the question in the heading above, you need to think about the following.

▶ What do cows and chickens do all day?

▶ How quickly can each move?

There are clearly big differences between the behaviour of cows and chickens. First, the cow generally stands around all day while the chicken moves round pecking at food. The cow is quite leisurely in its movement, but if you've ever tried to catch a chicken you'll know it can move pretty quickly. Chickens can fly but they can only maintain flight very briefly.

The cow needs muscle fibres that will provide the endurance to stand relatively still in a field for most of the day, so it consists of predominantly slow twitch muscle fibre. As slow twitch muscle fibres contain myoglobin and have many blood vessels, the cow's flesh will be red coloured. The breast of the chicken consists of fast twitch muscle fibres that enable it to move quickly and to take flight, hence the white coloured flesh. However, because the white, fast twitch fibres fatigue quickly, chickens can only fly for short periods of time. The legs of the chicken are darker in colour as they have a greater number of slow twitch fibres that enable the bird to stand for long periods of time and run if necessary.

TYPES OF MUSCLE ACTIONS

The term 'muscle actions' refers to two different things. Earlier in this chapter we talked about the specific movements that each muscle produces as 'muscle actions'. However, in this section, 'muscle actions' refers to specific ways that a muscle can develop tension. Up to this point, whenever I have talked about muscles producing tension I have referred to it as a 'muscle contraction'. Strictly speaking, this is incorrect because 'contraction' means shortening and muscles can develop tension in ways other than shortening. The term 'action' should be used when discussing how muscles develop tension. Muscles can develop tension or act in the following three ways.

▶ Concentric actions

A concentric muscle action occurs when the muscle shortens and develops tension, such as during the upwards movement of a bicep curl. In this case, the muscle develops tension to work against the force that gravity is exerting on the weight being lifted. The heavier the weight lifted, the greater gravity's pull and the greater force the muscle must produce. Concentric contractions are used to raise a weight, push off the ground or throw an implement (Hamill and Knutzen, 2007).

▶ Eccentric actions

An eccentric muscle action occurs when a muscle increases in length and develops tension. This type of action occurs predominantly to control the force of gravity. For example, on the downwards movement of the biceps curl, gravity will quickly return the weight towards the ground unless it is controlled by the action of the biceps muscle. The biceps brachii muscle will act eccentrically to control the movement of the elbow.

Eccentric muscle actions also play an important role in decelerating joints during movements. Take the example of the sprinter who uses his hip flexor muscles to flex his hip and drive his leg forwards with each stride. The hip flexors accelerate his leg forwards and at this point the hamstrings relax to allow the hip to flex. However, towards the end of the movement the hamstrings will start to act eccentrically to decelerate the movement at the hip joint before pulling the leg back and taking the next stride. The eccentric muscle action acts as a brake and is one of the reasons that hamstring muscles are injured during sprinting activities, as the muscle may not have enough eccentric strength to produce force for rapid deceleration.

▶ Isometric actions

An isometric action occurs when a muscle produces tension but its length does not change. To use the biceps curl example again, if the weight was held at a point halfway through the movement, the muscle would be developing tension without any movement occurring at the joint.

Isometric actions are common in the human body because they are needed to hold individual joints as well as the whole body in position. When standing up, the postural muscles, such as the calves, gluteals, abdominals and erector spinae, are all acting isometrically to hold the body still. After a while these muscles can start to ache as they fatigue. Postural abnormalities, such as a rounded back, are often the result of weaknesses in muscles that can no longer hold isometric actions against the force of gravity pushing down on them.

GROUP ACTION OF MUSCLES

When a muscle or muscle groups act to move the body or move a load they will not be working in isolation. Every movement involves the action of at least four muscles, each performing a different role. Muscles can perform one of four roles:

▶ agonist or prime mover – this is the muscle that develops tension to produce the joint movement

▶ antagonist – this is the muscle that relaxes, or stays relaxed if it is not contracting, to allow the joint movement to occur

▶ synergist – this is a muscle that assists the agonist to produce the joint movement

▶ neutralizer or fixator – these muscles act to hold the joint in position and eliminate any unwanted movement.

During a shoulder press, the shoulder joint goes through abduction. For this movement the deltoid is the agonist because it produces shoulder abduction. The latissimus dorsi is the antagonist that relaxes to allow the shoulder to adduct. There won't be a synergist for this movement but the trapezius will act as a neutralizer and hold the shoulder joint in position.

During the group action of muscles, different muscles act in different ways. The agonist and synergist act concentrically. The antagonist stays relaxed for most of the movement but is required to act eccentrically towards the end of the movement to decelerate the movement of the joint. Neutralizers act isometrically to hold the joint in position and prevent unwanted movement.

Neuromuscular physiology

All muscle actions and thus movements are controlled by the nervous system. The nervous system has two parts:

▶ the central nervous system (CNS), which consists of the brain and the spinal cord

▶ the peripheral nervous system (PNS), which consists of nerves that run from the spinal cord to the extremities of the body.

These systems deliver nervous impulses to and from muscles in the form of electrical currents. Efferent nerves, or motor neurones, deliver nervous impulses to the muscles. The nervous and muscular systems meet at the neuromuscular junction, as shown in Figure 2.11, where acetylcholine transmits the nervous impulse across the synaptic cleft into the muscle fibre.

Afferent nerves then send messages back to the brain about pressure and stretch within the muscles. Together the efferent and afferent nerves provide a feedback loop between the brain and muscles. In particular, the brain needs to know about the amount of stretch in a muscle so

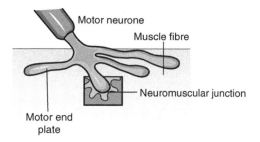

Figure 2.11 A motor neurone

that it can prevent the overstretching and tearing of muscle fibres. This communication uses muscle spindles that are found in muscles and Golgi tendon organs that are found in tendons.

▶ Muscle spindles

Muscle spindles are sensory receptors that are found in the belly of a muscle lying parallel to muscle fibres. They are attached to fasciculae by connective tissue. Their role is to sense changes in joint position, muscle length and muscle tension. In particular, when a muscle becomes stretched to the limit of its movement, the central nervous system initiates a muscular contraction to prevent it being stretched any further and potentially injured. This occurs at the level of the spinal cord rather than being processed higher up in the brain, and is called the *myotatic stretch reflex*, or just stretch reflex. It can be felt when you stretch a muscle, as the nerves will allow muscles to be stretched but when a certain point is reached, the muscle binds and stretching any further is very painful. The stretch reflex is also activated if a stretch is done too quickly; for example, if you bounce towards your toes the stretch reflex will be activated and you will bounce back upwards.

▶ Golgi tendon organs

Golgi tendon organs (GTOs) are found close to the junction between the tendon and the muscle. GTOs monitor tension within a muscle and they are activated to override or inhibit the stretch reflex. This is known as the *inverse stretch reflex* and GTOs cause the muscle that has been in a state of contraction to relax again. They allow the muscle to be stretched slightly further or loaded slightly more. The inverse stretch reflex takes around 10 seconds to be activated once the central nervous system has sensed that the muscle is not at risk of injury. When an athlete undertakes a developmental stretch, they will stretch the muscle until the muscle spindles are activated and then hold that position until the GTOs generate the inverse stretch reflex and relax. Then the muscle can be stretched slightly further until the muscle spindles activate the stretch reflex again. This process is done three or four times to increase the range of motion available at a joint.

Key point: The stretch reflex

The stretch reflex is activated by muscle spindles when they sense that the muscle is being stretched too far or too quickly.

The inverse stretch reflex is activated by Golgi tendon organs when they sense that the muscle can relax because it is not in danger of being damaged.

Production of energy in the body

Muscle fibres require energy to produce concentric, eccentric and isometric muscle actions. Other cells of the body require energy to produce nervous impulses, repair tissue, digest foods and circulate oxygenated blood around the body. All of these activities are powered by chemical energy in the forms of adenosine triphosphate (ATP) and phosphocreatine (PCr).

▶ Adenosine triphosphate (ATP)

ATP is an energy-rich compound which consists of one adenosine molecule attached to three phosphate molecules by high energy bonds, as seen in Figure 2.12. High energy bonds are represented by the squiggly lines.

$$A - P \sim P \sim P$$

Figure 2.12 Adenosine triphosphate (ATP)

These bonds are important as it is in these bonds that energy is stored; to release energy from ATP it is necessary to break one of the bonds. It is the third bond that is broken to release energy, and to enable the chemical reaction to occur two things are required:

▶ an enzyme is needed to act as a catalyst and speed up the reaction; this enzyme is called ATPase

▶ water; this is why the breakdown of ATP is also known as 'hydrolysis'.

Once ATP has been broken down to release energy, another compound is formed – adenosine diphosphate (ADP) – which is made up of the remaining adenosine molecules and the two phosphate molecules. This can be seen in Figure 2.13.

$$ATP + H_2O \xrightarrow{\text{ATPase}} ADP + P + E$$

Energy to cells

Figure 2.13 Hydrolysis of ATP into ADP and energy

Energy is released to the cells and the energy from ATP hydrolysis fuels, all the cells' functions; this is why ATP is described as the 'energy currency of the body' (McArdle, Katch and Katch, 2010).

Once ATP has been broken down to release its energy, it is no longer able to supply any further energy and therefore it needs to be resynthesized (reproduced). The component parts for ATP, which are ADP and phosphate (P), are still present in the cells but they need energy to reattach the free phosphate and resynthesize ATP. The energy needed to reattach the phosphate group is supplied by the breakdown of glucose and fats. The reattachment of the phosphate to ADP requires a second enzyme, ATPsynthase, as its catalyst, as seen in Figure 2.14.
This process happens over and over again to meet the energy needs of the cells. This is because the cells of the body can only store very limited amounts of ATP, about enough to provide 1–2 minutes of energy at rest. However, owing to resynthesis, the amount of ATP broken down and regenerated on a daily basis is roughly equivalent to an individual's body

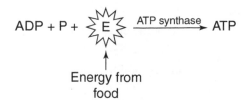

$$ADP + P + \text{E} \xrightarrow{\text{ATP synthase}} ATP$$

Energy from
food

Figure 2.14 The resynthesis of ATP

weight (Bursztyn, 1990). A marathon runner taking 2.5 hours to complete the distance will resynthesize around 80 kg of ATP during the run (McArdle, Katch and Katch, 2010).

Key point: ATP

ATP is adenosine triphosphate, an energy-rich compound that is the source of energy for muscular contraction and other functions of the human body that require energy.

It consists of one adenosine molecule attached to three phosphate molecules by high energy bonds. The energy in ATP is liberated when one of these high energy bonds is broken.

▶ Phosphocreatine (PCr)

Phosphocreatine is a second energy source available to cells. It is another high energy compound that releases energy very quickly and can provide both the energy and free phosphates to resynthesize ATP. PCr consists of a phosphate molecule and a creatine molecule attached by a high energy bond and this bond is broken, to liberate energy, by a reaction catalysed by an enzyme called creatine kinase. The chemical reaction is shown in Figure 2.15. The cells store enough PCr for 4–6 minutes of energy production at rest and about 5–7 seconds worth of work at maximum intensity. Overall the cells contain enough ATP and PCr for around 8–10 seconds of maximum intensity activity, such as sprinting.

$$PCr + ADP \xrightarrow{\text{Creatine kinase}} ATP + Cr$$

Figure 2.15 The splitting of phosphocreatine to liberate energy for ATP resynthesis

Although ATP can be resynthesized by the breakdown of PCr, there are two other ways that it can be resynthesized. These three methods of resynthesis are called the energy systems.

Spotlight: How does ATP contribute to the sliding filament model?

To produce a muscle contraction, cross bridges on myosin filaments must attach to actin. The contraction starts when ATP that is attached to myosin is broken down into ADP and phosphate. The energy that is released is used for the myosin head to extend and attach to the binding site on the actin. This triggers the power stroke where myosin pulls actin filaments together, causing the sarcomere to shorten in length. During the power stroke ADP and phosphate are released from the myosin filament, and the actin and myosin remain bound until a new molecule of ATP attaches to myosin. This frees myosin from the binding site and sends it back to its starting position. The myosin can now go through another cycle of binding to actin to produce another contraction, or it can remain unattached and allow the muscle to relax.

ENERGY STORES IN THE BODY

Apart from the tiny stores of ATP and PCr, the body is able to store potential energy in three forms:

▶ as glycogen (stored glucose) in the muscle and liver

▶ as fat in the form of stored body fat

▶ as protein in the structures of the body.

The body is very poor at storing glucose and the average person can only store around 2000 kcal of glycogen obtained from eating carbohydrates. Around 70 per cent of the body's glycogen is stored in skeletal muscle, with the other 30 per cent stored in the liver. There will also be glucose present in the bloodstream.

Spotlight: glucose or glycogen?

These words are often used interchangeably when discussing energy, to confusing effect.

Glucose, also called sugar, is the result of the breakdown of carbohydrates from the diet. Glucose is found in the bloodstream.

Glycogen is the term used for glucose that is being stored in the muscles and liver. It is found in a different form to glucose, as it needs to be combined with water to enable it to be stored.

Glycogen that is stored in the liver can return to the bloodstream as its main role is to keep the brain supplied with a steady supply of glucose. When glycogen enters the bloodstream it is once again referred to as glucose.

Fat is by far the body's largest store of potential energy, with the body storing around 100,000 kcal as fat. Fat is stored under the skin, around the kidneys and the heart. There are fats stored in the muscles as well. Energy becomes available from fat slowly because it takes a long time for it to be broken down. So while fat provides the majority of energy to the body at rest, it only becomes a useful source of energy after around 15–20 minutes of exercise (Bursztyn, 1990). Prior to this, the cells use glycogen as their energy source because it is more readily available, being broken down into energy more easily.

Protein can provide energy to cells, and an average 70 kg male can store around 24,000 kcal worth of energy as protein. However, because protein is stored primarily in structures of the body, it is not the body's preferred source of energy. The body will use some protein to liberate energy, especially in extreme endurance sports like a marathon, but extensive use of protein for energy results in damage to the body.

Cells are able to resynthesize ATP in two different ways: in the presence of oxygen (aerobically) and in the absence of oxygen (anaerobically). Whether ATP is resynthesized aerobically or anaerobically depends upon the length and intensity of an activity.

ENERGY SYSTEMS

In order to resynthesize ATP, the body has two systems that work anaerobically and one system that works aerobically. These systems are activated when receptors around the body sense a rise in ADP levels as they know that ATP has started to be broken down and that the body has very limited supplies of ATP. Initially PCr is broken down to provide the energy for resynthesis but the supply of this is very limited as well. Once stored PCr and ATP are used up, cells break down stored glucose for energy. Because extra oxygen is not yet available to the cells, this occurs anaerobically. After 2–3 minutes, oxygen becomes available to the contracting muscle cells and the body can gain energy for resynthesis aerobically. This process has used three energy systems: the ATP–PCr system, the lactic acid system and the aerobic system.

▶ ATP–PCr system

If the body rapidly goes from rest to performing high-intensity exercise, such as a 100 metre sprint or lifting a heavy weight, it will need energy very quickly. This energy comes from the muscular stores of ATP and PCr. The stored ATP is immediately broken down to liberate energy and the PCr is broken down to resynthesize this ATP. Once these stores have been depleted, energy has to be produced by another system and the intensity of exercise has to fall.

Consider Usain Bolt setting a world record for the 100 metres of 9.58 seconds in 2009; even he would be running out of energy to produce maximum speed by the end of the race. When he ran the distance in this world record time, he hit peak speed at between 60–70 metres, which he ran in 0.81 seconds. This is in comparison to his time for 90–100 metres, which was 0.83 seconds. Although it may have looked as if he was increasing his speed as he moved away from the other runners, in reality he was slowing down less quickly than the other runners.

Once PCr has been broken down to resynthesize ATP, it can be replaced by the breakdown of foods, such as carbohydrates, so that it is ready again to be broken down to provide energy to resynthesize more ATP. The ATP–PCr system recovers very quickly and ATP and PCr will be replenished after 4–5 minutes.

▶ Lactic acid system

To continue intense activity, ATP must be resynthesized in a different way. This is done by the lactic acid system. This system involves the breakdown of glycogen that is stored in the muscles through the process of anaerobic glycolysis. This process allows ATP to be resynthesized quickly but it produces lactic acid as a by-product. This is problematic because lactic acid accumulates in the working muscles and causes intense pain and a lack of coordination leading to a decrement in performance.

For example, 400 metre runners can be seen to slow down significantly during the last 100 metres of their race as lactic acid starts to accumulate. However, with training an athlete can run for longer at a high intensity without accumulating so much lactic acid or the intensity that lactic acid starts to build up can be increased. This is called lactate tolerance and training will raise the individual's lactate threshold (intensity where lactic acid starts to accumulate in the blood).

The lactic acid system is used in sports that demand moderate- to high-intensity activity over a period of between 1–2 minutes, such as 400 metre and 800 metre running, or sustained bursts of moderate to high activity with rest periods in between, for example sports such as football, rugby, tennis or badminton.

▶ Aerobic system

This system is often referred to as the oxygen system because it involves the breakdown of glycogen in the presence of oxygen. This is referred to as aerobic glycolysis and it produces more ATP per molecule of glucose than anaerobic glycolysis. This is because glucose can be completely broken down, rather than the partial breakdown that occurs in the lactic acid system, so that all bonds are broken down to release energy for ATP resynthesis.

Aerobic glycolysis resynthesizes 38 ATP from a molecule of glucose in comparison to 2 ATP resynthesized by anaerobic glycolysis.

A shortcoming of this system is that it takes a long time to deliver oxygen to the working muscles as the system releases energy relatively slowly. It is used in activities where energy is needed relatively slowly over a long period of time, such as during walking, long-distance running or swimming. This system can also produce energy through the breakdown of fats, which takes even longer than the breakdown of glycogen but releases even more energy to resynthesize ATP (129 ATP per molecule).

The breakdown of glucose or fat with oxygen will produce energy, water and carbon dioxide. However, the body is able to get rid of water and carbon dioxide through respiration and sweating. Consequently, the aerobic system produces no fatiguing waste products, unlike the lactic acid produced through the lactic acid system. Theoretically, as long as an athlete has the motivation to carry on, they could continue running at a steady speed indefinitely (McArdle, Katch and Katch, 2010).

Spotlight: Do different muscle fibre types use different energy systems?

Slow twitch muscle fibres are suited for endurance events as they have a good blood supply, many blood vessels and large number of mitochondria, which are parts of cells that produce energy. Slow twitch muscle fibres are totally dependent on the aerobic energy system for the production of ATP.

But what about fast twitch muscle fibres? Do they have two energy systems to produce ATP?

Well, yes and no! There are actually two different type of slow twitch muscle fibres – type IIa and type IIx (sometimes referred to as IIb). Type IIa fibres produce medium to high force and are more resistant to fatigue than type IIx. Type IIa fibres rely most heavily on the lactic acid system, although they do have some aerobic capability so they can also use the aerobic system. Type IIx fibres work at intensities of around 90–100 per cent of maximum and are almost totally reliant on the ATP–PCr system for the resynthesis of ATP as a result.

INTERACTION OF THE ENERGY SYSTEMS

While different energy systems provide ATP for activities of different intensity, in reality they all work together.

Take the example of a 1500 metre runner. When the runner starts, they need energy quickly to provide the spark to get going. The ATP–PCr and lactic acid systems provide the initial ATP for this. As the race progresses the contribution of these energy systems reduces as the contribution of the aerobic system increases. During the middle phase of the race the aerobic system resynthesizes most of the ATP. However, towards the end of the race the athlete may want to increase their speed and produce a sprint finish. At this point the aerobic system is working at its full capacity so the extra ATP the body needs is resynthesized by the lactic acid system and then finally the ATP–PCr system.

A footballer, for example, would use all three systems at different times. The ATP–PCr system provides the extra energy needed to sprint, jump, kick or throw the ball. The lactic acid system would be used when running around the pitch as footballers tend to run at just below top speed. But these runs are interspersed with periods of walking or jogging. Football players rely on the lactic acid system predominantly for their energy production.

Key point: The energy systems

Energy systems are used to resynthesize ATP so it can be broken down to release more energy. There are three energy systems:

▶ the ATP–PCr system relies on the breakdown of stored ATP and PCr to resynthesize ATP

▶ the lactic acid system relies on the anaerobic breakdown of glycogen to resynthesize ATP (anaerobic glycolysis)

▶ the aerobic system relies on the aerobic breakdown of glycogen to resynthesize ATP (aerobic glycolysis).

Dig deeper

Online resources

About Health (article on fast and slow twitch muscle fibres)

http://sportsmedicine.about.com/od/anatomyandphysiology/a/MuscleFiberType.htm

BBC Science

www.bbc.co.uk/science/humanbody/body/factfiles/skeleton_anatomy.shtml

Get Body Smart

www.getbodysmart.com

Healthline

www.healthline.com/human-body-maps/skeletal-system

Inner Body

www.innerbody.com

Books

E.N. Marieb, *The Essentials of Human Anatomy and Physiology*, 8th edn (San Francisco: Pearson Education, 2006).

W.D. McArdle, F.I. Katch and V.L. Katch, *Exercise Physiology: Nutrition, Energy, and Human Performance*, 7th edn (Baltimore, MD: Lippincott, Williams and Wilkins, 2010).

S. Parker, *The Human Body* (London: Dorling Kindersley, 2007).

D. Sewell, P. Watkins and M. Griffin, *Sport and Exercise Science: An Introduction*, 2nd edn (Abingdon: Hodder Arnold, 2012).

G.J. Tortora and B. Derrickson, *Introduction to the Human Body: The essentials of anatomy and physiology*, 7th edn (New York: John Wiley, 2007).

Fact-check

1 Which of the following is *not* a function of the skeleton?
   a   Attachment sites
   b   Production of nervous impulses
   c   Levers for movement
   d   Provision of structural support

2 How many bones make up the appendicular skeleton?
   a   122
   b   124
   c   126
   d   128

3 What type of bone is the sternum?
   a   Long
   b   Flat
   c   Irregular
   d   Short

4 Which type of synovial joint allows movement in three planes?
   a   Ball and socket
   b   Hinge
   c   Pivot
   d   Condyloid

5 Movement of a body part away from the body is known as:
   a   Flexion
   b   Extension
   c   Abduction
   d   Adduction

6 The muscle covering the shoulder is called:
   a   Trapezius
   b   Pectoralis major
   c   Latissimus dorsi
   d   Deltoids

7 The outer layer of the muscle is called:
   a   Sarcomere
   b   Perimysium
   c   Epimysium
   d   Endomysium

8 Which of the following is a feature of fast twitch muscle fibres?
   a   Whitish in colour
   b   Good blood supply
   c   Slow to fatigue
   d   Used for endurance activities

9 Which of the following roles describes the muscle(s) that act to hold a joint in position?

    a   Agonist

    b   Antagonist

    c   Synergist

    d   Fixator

10 Which of the following energy systems is able to resynthesize ATP at the fastest rate?

    a   Aerobic system

    b   ATP–PCr system

    c   Lactic acid system

    d   Oxygen system

3

Key principles in anatomy and physiology 2: The cardio-respiratory system

In order to survive and carry out their vital functions, the cells of the human body require a steady supply of oxygen. They also need to remove the waste product, carbon dioxide, as its build-up creates a weak acid that is toxic to the body. To achieve these twin aims, the respiratory system and the cardiovascular system work together to form a system commonly referred to as the cardio-respiratory system.

Athletes refer to these systems as their 'engine' or 'engine room' as they are responsible for providing the muscles with the oxygen and nutrients required to produce energy. The efficiency of these two systems has a direct effect on the athlete's cardiovascular, or aerobic, fitness and thus influences the intensity and duration of their performance.

The respiratory system introduces oxygen into the bloodstream and the cardiovascular system is responsible for delivering oxygenated blood to the muscles, brain and wherever else it is required in the body.

This chapter will examine the structures that make up these two systems and how they function. Chapter 4 will expand on this information by looking at how the systems respond to exercise and the effect that training has on their physiology.

The respiratory system

The respiratory system is responsible for pulmonary ventilation, or breathing, and brings inhaled air into contact with blood so that oxygen can be absorbed and carbon dioxide removed. It consists of all the structures from the nose and mouth down to the alveoli, which are tiny structures in the lungs where gases are exchanged (gaseous exchange).

The respiratory system performs other functions as well as gaseous exchange. The act of exhaling air also removes some water and heat from the body; the water can be seen when we exhale air on a cold day. The respiratory system has to filter, warm and moisten air as air goes from a cold, dirty, dry external environment into a warm, clean, moist internal environment. The respiratory system also provides us with a sense of smell and allows us to produce sounds and noises.

ANATOMY OF THE RESPIRATORY SYSTEM

The respiratory system is able to provide the body with around 360 litres of oxygen a day, which has been extracted from 10,000 litres of air. To enable it to do this, air must pass through a series of structures, which are effectively passageways of decreasing diameter. The two lungs are the major organs of the respiratory system and they are connected to the external environment via the bronchi and the trachea. They are vulnerable organs and are protected by the ribs, which are a series of flat bones, and by the muscles of the chest. The right lung is slightly larger than the left because the left lung has a space, called the cardiac notch, which allows it to house the heart. The action of the respiratory system is controlled by the respiratory centre in the brain. Figure 3.1 shows the major structures of the respiratory system.

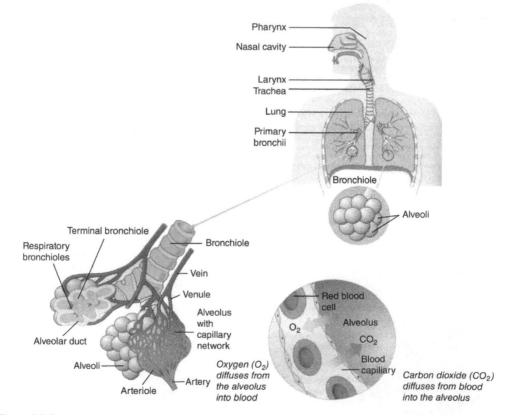

Figure 3.1 The major structures of the respiratory system

▶ Nose and mouth

The nose is the only external part of the respiratory system and air enters the nose through two nares, or nostrils. The interior of the nose contains thick hairs and three ridges called conchae. The conchae contain many capillaries where inhaled air comes into contact with warmth from the blood circulating in the capillaries to raise its temperature. The hairs, in conjunction with mucus produced by the mucus membranes that line the inner surface of the nose, moisten the air and trap any particles of dirt or dust. The nose also contains many olfactory receptors that detect smells. The nose delivers the warmed and moistened air to the throat through two internal nares.

▶ Pharynx

The pharynx, or throat, lies behind the nose and mouth and is about 12 cm in length. Its walls are made of skeletal muscle and are lined with mucus membranes to keep them moist. It acts as a passageway for food as well as air. At the terminal point of the pharynx, food will enter the oesophagus and air will enter the larynx.

▶ Larynx

The larynx is the voice box and is situated below the pharynx and just in front of the fourth, fifth and sixth cervical vertebrae. It is made of eight pieces of hard cartilage. The epiglottis, which is a spoon-shaped flap of cartilage positioned at the top of the larynx, forms a lid over the larynx when we swallow food. If any food or liquid enters the larynx, we produce the cough reflex to expel food and prevent us from choking. The vocal cords are two folds of the mucus membranes that line the larynx and they vibrate when air is expelled to produce sounds.

▶ Trachea

The trachea, or windpipe, is a firm, cartilaginous tube that travels from the larynx to the entrance to the lungs. It is made up of C-shaped rings of cartilage that provide protection and keep the trachea open despite the changes in pressure in the trachea. The oesophagus, which is the tube that takes food to the stomach, runs directly behind the trachea. The open section of the C-shaped rings contains the oesophagus and this space allows it to expand when food is swallowed.

▶ Bronchus

Where the trachea meets the lungs it divides into the left primary bronchus and the right primary bronchus. These bronchi deliver air into each lung and are also made up of firm C-shaped rings of cartilage. These primary bronchi very quickly subdivide into secondary bronchi that lead to the different lobes within each lung. The right lung, being slightly larger, has three lobes while the left lung has two.

▶ Bronchioles

In the lungs, the bronchi subdivide 23 times to make up around eight million terminal bronchioles in each lung. Bronchioles are smaller versions of the bronchi and as they subdivide they become smaller and smaller, with some bronchi measuring less than 1 mm in diameter (Burstzyn, 1990). The bronchi and bronchioles resemble a tree where the trunk divides into smaller and smaller branches. As a result, the airways in the lungs are often referred to as the 'bronchial tree'. The walls of the bronchi are made up of cartilage and smooth muscle, but as their branches become increasingly smaller the cartilage disappears and they consist of predominantly smooth muscle. This smooth muscle can contract to help push air along the airways.

▶ Alveoli

Each bronchiole terminates at a cluster of around 30–40 alveoli. In each lung there are around 600 million alveoli (Burstzyn, 1990) and these terminal points of the lungs are where gaseous exchange between the lungs and blood occurs. Each alveolus is surrounded by a network of tiny capillaries where oxygen enters the blood from the alveoli, and carbon dioxide is transferred into the alveoli from the blood.

▶ Lungs

The lungs themselves are positioned within the ribcage and are closed off at the top by the clavicle and muscle around it. At the bottom of the chest they are sealed by the diaphragm, which is a large sheet of muscle that covers the bottom of the ribcage. The lungs are enclosed by the pleural membrane, which is also present on the back of the ribs. The two surfaces of the pleural membrane are connected by the pleural fluid that is present in the pleural space. Thus, the lungs stick to the back of the ribs rather than being fixed in position. This is one of the reasons that lungs can collapse if they are punctured. If this is the case, the lungs need to be inflated again to allow them to reattach to the back of the ribs. The movement of the ribs is one of the mechanisms of respiration, or breathing.

MECHANISMS OF RESPIRATION

Respiration is more complex than it may initially seem. Inspiration and expiration of air occur owing to pressure changes in the lungs. Inspiration is the result of the volume of the chest cavity increasing and the pressure within it falling. This decrease in pressure causes air to be drawn in. During expiration the chest cavity decreases in volume and the internal pressure increases, causing air to be forced out.

The changes in volume, or size, of the chest cavity are the result of the action of skeletal muscles. The chest cavity's volume is increased in two ways:

▶ first, by the flattening of the diaphragm. The diaphragm is a large dome-like muscle that covers the bottom of the chest cavity and when it contracts, it flattens and causes an increase in the volume of the chest cavity. This is described as 'stomach breathing', as it can be seen to occur in the stomach area.

▶ second, the movement of the ribs outwards and upwards causes the volume of the chest cavity to increase. The ribs are moved by intercostal muscles (*intercostal* meaning 'between ribs') and there are two sets of these muscles. The external intercostal muscles are arranged so that when they contract they push the chest outwards and upwards causing inspiration. The internal intercostal muscles force the lungs downwards and cause air to be expelled.

The intercostal muscles are responsible for 'chest breathing' along with other skeletal muscles which become active when breathing deepens. The pectoralis minor, sternocleidomastoid and scalene muscles act to elevate the ribs and sternum.

At rest and low levels of activity the contraction of the diaphragm, as seen in Figure 3.2, is responsible for about 75 per cent of the air inhaled (Tortora and Derrickson, 2007). However, the action of the diaphragm can be impeded if a person is pregnant, obese or has eaten a heavy meal. This can cause shortness of breath or laboured chest breathing. At intense levels of exercise the body's need for more air is met by the action of the external intercostal muscles and associated muscles that move the ribs.

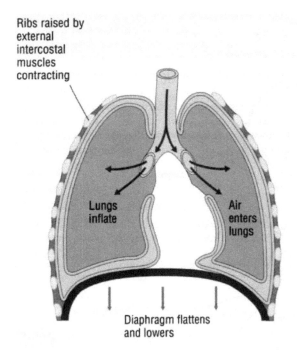

Ribs raised by external intercostal muscles contracting

Lungs inflate

Air enters lungs

Diaphragm flattens and lowers

Figure 3.2 Movement of the diaphragm during inhalation

At rest, exhalation is a passive process, meaning that skeletal muscle contractions are not needed. Exhalation only becomes an active process when breathing becomes forceful, such as when running quickly or when blowing up a balloon. Forceful exhalation is the responsibility of the internal intercostal muscles, assisted by other skeletal muscles such as the obliques, transverse abdominis and the rectus abdominis. They act to force the ribs downwards and, in conjunction with the diaphragm relaxing and moving upwards, the space in the lungs decreases, forcing air out.

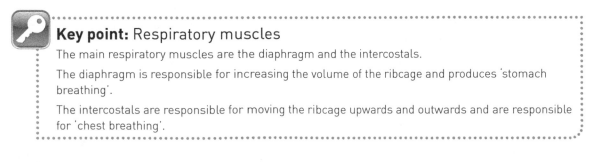

Key point: Respiratory muscles

The main respiratory muscles are the diaphragm and the intercostals.

The diaphragm is responsible for increasing the volume of the ribcage and produces 'stomach breathing'.

The intercostals are responsible for moving the ribcage upwards and outwards and are responsible for 'chest breathing'.

Spotlight: What causes the breathing rate to increase?

Breathing rate is controlled by the brain and nervous system. It is under the unconscious control of the respiratory centre that is found in the medulla oblongata.

The respiratory centre receives information from chemoreceptors around the body. They are found in the heart and the carotid artery, which is in the neck. They monitor the acidity of the blood because the body ceases to function if its internal environment becomes too acidic.

When the body starts to produce more energy, such as during exercise, more carbon dioxide is produced by the aerobic energy system. The breakdown of glucose in the presence of oxygen produces energy but also carbon dioxide and water. The carbon dioxide becomes dissolved in water, forming carbonic acid. This weak acid raises the pH of the body and this is picked up by the chemoreceptors, which respond by raising the breathing to expel more carbon dioxide and restore blood pH.

The nerves between the respiratory centre and the respiratory muscles carry impulses that stimulate an increase in the breathing rate by causing the respiratory muscles to contract. The phrenic nerve sends messages to the diaphragm while the intercostal nerves send messages to the intercostals. As carbon dioxide is exhaled, the pH of the blood is restored to an acceptable level.

Increases in breathing rate also incidentally result in an increased amount of oxygen being introduced into the body. This increase in the supply of oxygen is used by the muscles to produce more energy; however, the body has not responded to the increased demand for oxygen but rather to the increased production of carbon dioxide.

▶ **Lung volume and capacities**

The maximum amount of air our lungs could hold is around 5 litres, which is equivalent to the amount of air in a basketball. This figure can be slightly higher for a man and slightly lower for a woman. We are only able to expel a maximum of around 4 litres of air or else our lungs would collapse. The 1 litre remaining in the lungs is called the residual volume. The amount of air we inhale with each breath is referred to as the tidal volume. At rest, we have a tidal volume of around 0.5 litre of air with each breath and on average we take between 10–12 breaths per minute. This means that at rest we pass between 5–6 litres of air per minute through our lungs. The volume of air breathed per minute is referred to as minute ventilation. During exercise the amount of air that we breathe in and out and the number of breaths we take increase significantly.

The maximum volume of air that can be inhaled and exhaled is the vital capacity and as exercise intensity increases, the tidal volume becomes larger and can increase until vital capacity is reached. Breathing rate can increase significantly as well, rising to 30 breaths per minute for moderate intensity exercise and up to 50 breaths per minute for intense exercise (McArdle, Katch and Katch, 2010).

If tidal volume were to increase to 4 litres per breath and breathing rate to 50 breaths per minute, then the volume of air passing through the lungs per minute (minute ventilation) is increased to 200 litres per minute. This is a significant increase on minute volume of 5 litres at rest. There are several other measures of lung function and capacity and these are shown in Figure 3.3 and explained in Table 3.1.

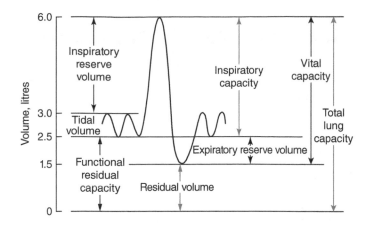

Figure 3.3 Lung volumes and capacities

Table 3.1 Lung volume and capacities explained

Lung volume/capacity	Explanation
Total lung capacity	The volume of air in the lungs after a maximum inhalation
Tidal volume	The volume of air in each breath
Residual volume	The volume of air left in the lungs after a full exhalation
Vital capacity	The maximum volume of air that can be inhaled and exhaled in one breath
Inspiratory reserve volume	The volume of air that can be inhaled in addition to tidal volume
Expiratory reserve volume	The volume of air that can be exhaled in addition to tidal volume
Functional residual capacity	Potential amount of additional air that can be exhaled
Inspiratory capacity	Additional volume of air that can be exhaled without using any residual capacity

Lung function can adapt with exercise but actual capacity is limited by the size of an individual's ribcage; because this cannot increase, the size of the lungs cannot increase. However, the respiratory muscles will act like other skeletal muscles that adapt to exercise by becoming larger and stronger. Thus the lungs can be become more efficient and move more air in and out with each breath. This will be examined in greater detail in Chapter 4.

▶ Exchange of oxygen and carbon dioxide in the lungs

Diffusion is the term used to refer to the process of gaseous exchange that occurs in the lungs. Gaseous exchange involves oxygen and carbon dioxide and has two functions:

▶ to replenish the blood with oxygen so that it can be taken to the muscles and other tissues that require it

▶ to remove from the blood carbon dioxide that is the result of energy production in the muscles and other tissues.

Inhaled air contains a number of gases (Table 3.2). The main gas in air is nitrogen, which is not absorbed by the blood so it is all exhaled. Inhaled air has 21 per cent oxygen, of which the blood can take in a small amount and the rest is exhaled. Because exhaled air still has high levels of oxygen, we can use exhaled oxygen to resuscitate someone else. Exhaled air has an increased amount of carbon dioxide that has replaced oxygen. There are also small amounts of inert gases, such as argon, neon, helium and methane.

Table 3.2 The composition of air

Gas	Inhaled air	Exhaled air	Difference
Nitrogen	78%	78%	0%
Oxygen	21%	17%	4% decrease
Carbon dioxide	0.03%	4%	4% increase
Other gases	0.9%	0.9%	0%

▶ Partial pressure of gases

The concept of partial pressure is central to an understanding of gaseous exchange. Partial pressure is described as the individual pressure a gas exerts within a mixture of gases. Each gas will exert a pressure that is proportional to its concentration within the whole gas. The partial pressures of each individual gas within a mixture will equal the total pressure of the gas.

Inhaled air consists of three main gases in different percentages: nitrogen at 78 per cent, oxygen at 21 per cent and carbon dioxide at 0.03 per cent. These percentages represent their concentration in atmospheric air. The atmospheric pressure at sea level is 769 mmHg and this represents the pressure atmospheric air exerts on the ground. However, within the air as a whole, each gas is responsible for exerting pressure on its own. For example, oxygen is responsible for 21 per cent of the atmospheric air and its partial pressure can be calculated by finding 21 per cent of overall atmospheric pressure:

Partial pressure of oxygen (pO^2) = atmospheric pressure × percentage of oxygen
$pO^2 = 769 × 0.21 = 161.49$ mmHg

Partial pressure will account for the movement of gases between the alveoli and the capillaries, as well as the movement of gases between the capillaries and muscles.

▶ Gaseous exchange in the lungs

The movement of gases between the alveoli and the blood is due to an imbalance between their relative concentrations. In the alveoli, there is a higher concentration of oxygen (pO^2 of 105 mmHg) than in the blood contained within the capillaries (pO^2 of 40 mmHg). This difference creates a pressure gradient. The capillaries that surround the alveoli are only one cell thick and there are tiny spaces between the cells in the artery walls that allow gases to pass through them. The difference in the pressure of oxygen forces oxygen from the alveoli into the blood until the pressure is equal in both the lungs and the blood.

The partial pressure of carbon dioxide (pCO^2) is also different between the lungs and the blood. Air in the lungs has a low pCO^2 of 5 mmHg compared to the pCO^2 of 45 mmHg in the capillaries. This pressure differential causes carbon dioxide to move from the blood to the alveoli where it can be exhaled. This movement of gases is referred to as diffusion.

Once the lungs have oxygenated the blood it becomes the responsibility of the cardiovascular system to deliver the oxygenated blood around the body.

Spotlight: Diffusion – how gases move

Diffusion is the movement of a gas from an area of higher partial pressure to an area of lower partial pressure.

All gases move by diffusion. For example, if someone sprays perfume or aftershave on their body, it will be smelled by other people in a room because it diffuses from an area where its partial pressure is high (on their body) to an area where the partial pressure is lower (in the rest of the room).

In the body, oxygen and carbon dioxide change places by diffusing from areas of high partial pressure to areas of low partial pressure. Diffusion takes place in two areas of the body. It occurs in the lungs to introduce oxygen into the bloodstream and it occurs in the muscles (and other tissues) when oxygen moves out of the bloodstream and carbon dioxide moves into it. In the muscles and tissues, oxygen is used to produce energy.

Diffusion of gases in the lungs is often referred to as 'external respiration' while diffusion in other tissues, such as the muscles, is referred to as 'internal respiration'.

The cardiovascular system

The cardiovascular system is also referred to as the circulatory system and is responsible for delivering nutrients, oxygen and water to tissues as well as transporting hormones and enzymes around the body. It also takes waste products, such as carbon dioxide and lactic acid, away from the tissues of the body to be expelled or broken down. The cardiovascular system consists of three components:

▶ the blood, which is the fluid carrying oxygen and nutrients around the body

▶ the heart, which acts as a pump to propel the blood around the body

▶ the blood vessels, which provide tubes for the blood to travel through on its journey to and from the heart.

THE BLOOD

Blood is a thick, red-coloured fluid that will be bright red when it is oxygenated and a darker red when it has been deoxygenated. Blood accounts for around 8 per cent of our body weight, and on average a man has a blood volume of 5–6 litres and a woman has a blood volume of 3–4 litres (Tortora and Derrickson, 2007). Blood has four main functions.

1 Transportation – the blood transports oxygen, nutrients and water around the body and carries away waste products for excretion.

2 Regulation of temperature – the blood helps to regulate temperature (thermoregulation) by taking heat away from muscles and other tissues. It takes warm blood close to the surface of the body so it can be released through the skin by radiation.

3 Protection against injury – blood will clot in response to an injury where blood vessels are damaged and prevent haemorrhaging.

4 Fighting infection – the blood contains white cells and proteins called antibodies that will help fight infection and protect against disease.

▶ **The composition of blood**

Despite seeming to be a fluid, blood consists of both fluid and solid parts. The fluid part is called plasma, which is pale yellow in colour and provides the liquid for the solid components to float in. It makes up 55 per cent of the blood volume. The other 45 per cent of blood volume is made up of blood cells, of which there are three types: red blood cells (erythrocytes), white blood cells (leucocytes) and platelets (thrombocytes). Around 99 per cent of the solids in the blood are red blood cells, and the white blood cells and platelets account for the remaining 1 per cent of solids. The breakdown of the components of blood can be seen in Figure 3.4.

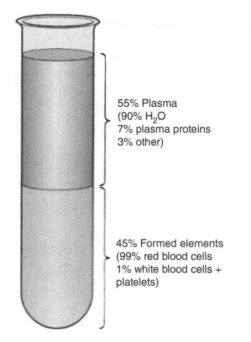

55% Plasma
(90% H$_2$O
7% plasma proteins
3% other)

45% Formed elements
(99% red blood cells
1% white blood cells +
platelets)

Figure 3.4 The components of blood

Because of the high volume of solids or cells present in the blood, it is a thick liquid, described as being viscous. Its viscosity means that it slowly oozes from a small cut rather than pouring out like water. The more viscous a fluid becomes, the more resistant to flowing it will become. If we become dehydrated, the plasma content of the blood decreases and the solid content increases proportionally, and this means that it will not circulate as easily around the body. This is problematic during endurance-based exercise or exercise in the heat as performance will be negatively affected. Likewise, an increase in the red blood cell count, which may occur naturally as a result of training (particularly at altitude) or illegally through blood doping, could be problematic. In reality, when the red blood cell count increases as a training adaptation, the blood plasma volume increases as well to prevent blood becoming more viscous.

Red blood cells

Red blood cells, as seen in Figure 3.5, are tiny, disc-like bodies that are concave on both sides. There are millions of red blood cells in the blood with about 5 million present in every cubic millimetre of blood. Their main feature is that they contain a protein called haemoglobin,

Figure 3.5 A red blood cell

which appears to be red in colour. The pigment is actually yellow but it has a massed effect of making the blood look red. Haemoglobin has a massive attraction for oxygen. As it passes through the capillaries around the alveoli, haemoglobin combines with the oxygen present in the alveoli to form oxyhaemoglobin and become bright red in colour.

The sole function of red blood cells is to transport oxygen to the tissues of the body and their success is dependent on the quantity of haemoglobin they contain. A reduction in the amount of haemoglobin present can result in a condition called anaemia, where the oxygen-carrying capacity of the blood is reduced.

Red blood cells are produced in the red bone marrow of spongy bone that is found at the ends of long bones, as well as in flat and irregular bones. The production of red blood cells is referred to as *erythropoiesis*. A red blood cell has a lifespan of around 120 days before being removed from circulation by the spleen and lymph nodes. Red blood cell production and removal occur at roughly the same rate to ensure the red blood cell count remains constant.

White blood cells

White blood cells, as seen in Figure 3.6, are larger and less numerous than red blood cells. Red blood cells outnumber white blood cells by a ratio of 700:1. White blood cells defend the body against damage from bacteria, viruses and tumours. Their number increases significantly within a few hours when an infection is present in the body. Unlike red blood cells, the white blood cells can leave the blood vessels and move to wherever infection is present. The cardiovascular system is merely a transport system for them. They respond to chemicals given off by damaged tissues by moving to that area to destroy any microorganisms that are present.

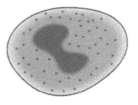

Figure 3.6 A white blood cell

White blood cells are also produced in red bone marrow but they have a much shorter lifespan of only a few days. This is because bacteria are continually entering the body through the nose and mouth and white blood cells are destroyed when they perform their functions. At times of infection some white blood cells may only have a lifespan of a few hours.

Platelets

Platelets, as seen in Figure 3.7, are even smaller than red blood cells and are made in the bone marrow. They are responsible for clotting the blood and turn sticky when they are exposed to air or to a rough, damaged surface. They prevent blood loss when blood vessels are damaged.

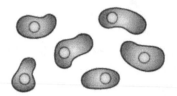

Figure 3.7 Platelets

> ### 🔑 **Key point:** Components of the blood
>
> Blood is made up of fluid and solid components. The fluid component is plasma, which accounts for 55 per cent of blood volume. The solid component consists of red blood cells, white blood cells and platelets, which account for the remaining 45 per cent.
>
> Red blood cells transport oxygen, white blood cells fight infection and platelets help to clot blood.

THE HEART

The heart is a hollow, muscular organ that is responsible for pumping blood to the tissues where oxygen and other nutrients are needed. It is located behind the sternum, with two-thirds of it towards the left-hand side. The heart beats at a rate of 60–80 times per minute, or around 100,000 times a day, to propel blood through the vast network of blood vessels. The heart is described as a double-action pump which has two sides separated by a thick wall, called the septum. The left-hand side pumps blood around the body while the right-hand side pumps blood through the lungs to be oxygenated. The two sides of the heart have no communication with each other; however, each side has two chambers which do communicate with each other. Each side has a receiving, or holding, chamber called an atrium (plural: *atria*) and a pumping chamber called a ventricle. Each atrium communicates with its ventricle through a one-way valve, called the atrio-ventricular valve. These valves prevent the backflow of blood from the ventricle to the atrium when the ventricles contract forcefully. The structure of the heart can be seen in Figure 3.8.

The heart is made of a specialist type of muscle, called cardiac muscle, and is also referred to as the myocardium. The myocardium varies in thickness: it is thicker around the ventricles and thinner around the atria. It needs to be thicker around the ventricles to provide power to eject blood at a high pressure so it can travel to the extremities of the body. The heart is surrounded by a structure called the pericardium, which anchors to the back of the sternum and to the diaphragm, so it is held firmly in place.

▶ The heart as a double-action pump

The heart is divided into sides; the left side is responsible for pumping oxygenated blood to the body and the right side for pumping deoxygenated blood to the lungs. It is vital that oxygenated and deoxygenated blood are kept apart and this is the role of the septum.

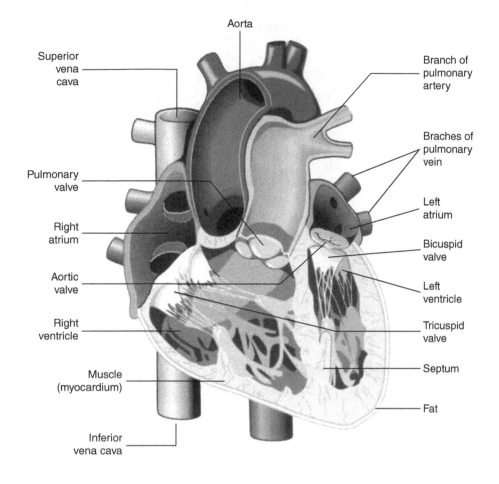

Aorta

Superior vena cava

Branch of pulmonary artery

Braches of pulmonary vein

Pulmonary valve

Left atrium

Right atrium

Bicuspid valve

Aortic valve

Left ventricle

Right ventricle

Tricuspid valve

Muscle (myocardium)

Septum

Fat

Inferior vena cava

Figure 3.8 The structure of the heart

The left side of the heart is responsible for systemic circulation, i.e. pumping oxygen-rich blood to the tissues of the body. At rest, the blood flows to the major organs of the body – the liver, kidneys and brain each use around 20 per cent of the blood flow. The liver is the most metabolically active organ in the body and is particularly active after a meal when it is heavily involved in digestion. The kidneys have a large flow of blood so that they can regulate blood volume and blood pressure, while the brain needs a steady supply of oxygen and glucose to function effectively. The muscles also have around 20 per cent of the blood volume, and blood also flows to the skin for cooling off and to the heart muscle itself to provide energy for the contraction of the heart.

The right side of the heart is responsible for pulmonary circulation between the heart and the lungs. Oxygen-poor blood is pumped from the right ventricle to the lungs, where carbon dioxide is expelled and the blood is replenished with a fresh supply of oxygen. The systemic and pulmonary circulation can be seen in Figure 3.9.

Blood flow into, through, and out of the heart is dependent on a series of valves that are present at the openings into and out of the heart and in between the chambers.

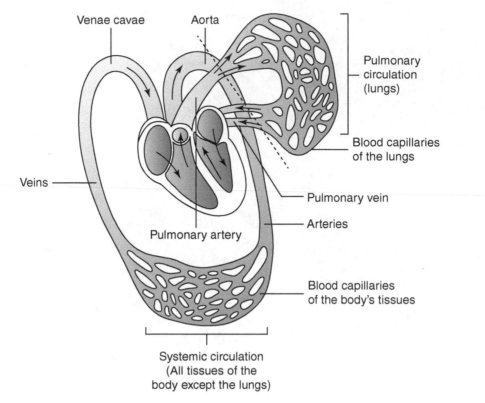

Venae cavae

Aorta

Pulmonary circulation (lungs)

Blood capillaries of the lungs

Veins

Pulmonary vein

Arteries

Pulmonary artery

Blood capillaries of the body's tissues

Systemic circulation (All tissues of the body except the lungs)

Figure 3.9 The systemic and pulmonary circuits of blood flow

▶ The valves of the heart

The heart utilizes valves to keep blood flowing in the right direction through the heart. There are four main valves. The tricuspid, or right atrio-ventricular valve, is positioned between the right atrium and right ventricle. It consists of three triangular flaps or cusps that are positioned to be forced closed when the right ventricle contracts and blood is pushed against them. However, once the right ventricle has pumped, it will relax and receive blood from the right atrium so it becomes full in preparation for the next contraction. The right atrium pumps blood through the tricuspid valve before it closes again to prevent blood being forced back through it.

The bicuspid or left atrio-ventricular valve is positioned between the left atrium and the left ventricle. It is also called the mitral valve. It is slightly smaller than the tricuspid valve as it has only two triangular cusps (hence its name; 'bi' refers to two and 'cuspid' to the cusps). It acts in the same way as the tricuspid valve, as it is forced shut when the powerful left ventricle contracts and it opens when the left ventricle relaxes and the left atrium pumps blood through the mitral valve.

The aortic valve is positioned between the left ventricle and the aorta, which is the main blood vessel leaving the heart. It has two cusps that are attached to the walls of the arteries. As blood flows out of the left ventricle the cusps are forced back against the walls of the aorta but once the contraction has passed, the cusps fall back to block the exit of the heart and prevent blood flowing back into the left ventricle from the aorta.

The pulmonary valve is located between the right ventricle and the pulmonary artery, which is the large artery that takes blood to the lungs. It works in the same way as the aortic valve as it is forced open when the right ventricle ejects blood into the pulmonary artery and closes once the contraction has passed. Figure 3.10 shows a simplified version of the location of the chambers and valves of the heart.

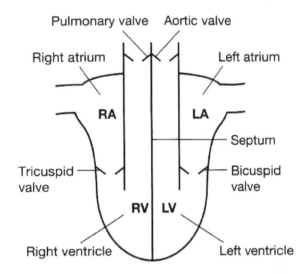

Figure 3.10 The location of the chambers and valves of the heart

Key point: The chambers and valves of the heart

The atria are collecting chambers, where blood waits before entering the ventricles. The ventricles are pumps that provide force to propel blood around the body:

▶ right atrium – receives deoxygenated blood from the body

▶ right ventricle – pumps deoxygenated blood to the lungs

▶ left atrium – receives oxygenated blood from the lungs

▶ left ventricle – pumps oxygenated blood to the organs of the body.

Valves allow blood to flow in one direction and they open and close in response to the pressure of blood flow:

▶ tricuspid valve is positioned between the right atrium and right ventricle

▶ bicuspid valve is positioned between the left atrium and left ventricle

▶ aortic valve is positioned between the left ventricle and aorta

▶ pulmonary valve is positioned between the right ventricle and the pulmonary artery.

MAJOR BLOOD VESSELS LEADING INTO AND OUT OF THE HEART

Deoxygenated blood is delivered back to the heart through a series of veins and these will eventually drain into two major veins entering the heart. From the areas below the heart, blood returns to the heart through the inferior vena cava. From areas above the heart, blood returns to the heart through the superior vena cava. These venae cavae pour blood simultaneously into the right atrium, which then contracts to pump blood into the right ventricle. From the right ventricle, this deoxygenated blood is pumped to the lungs via the pulmonary artery. The pulmonary artery is the only artery that carries deoxygenated blood.

In the lungs the blood becomes oxygenated and returns to the heart via the pulmonary vein; the pulmonary vein is the only vein that carries oxygenated blood. It enters the left atrium before being pumped into the left ventricle where oxygenated blood is pumped into the aorta. The aorta is a large, thick-walled artery that starts the blood on its journey around the body. These major blood vessels can be seen in Figure 3.11.

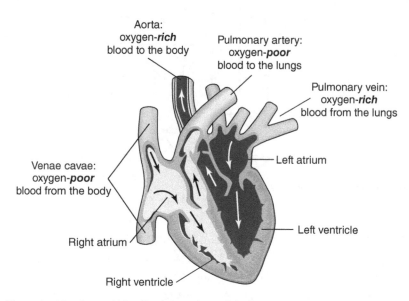

Figure 3.11 The major blood vessels leading into and out of the heart

Spotlight: Coronary arteries – the crowning glory!

Coronary arteries are the arteries that actually supply the heart muscle, or myocardium, itself. The arteries are called 'coronary arteries' because they sit on top of the heart muscle like a crown.

The heart supplies itself with the most oxygen-rich blood available because these coronary arteries branch off the aorta almost immediately after the blood has passed through the aortic valve. The heart knows that its own continued function is central to the survival of the body as a whole, therefore it needs the best blood supply.

The blood supplied to the heart muscle has newly arrived from the lungs, where it has been oxygenated. However, it can also contain toxins that have been breathed in from the environment. For example, cigarette smoke contains thousands of toxic substances that are damaging to tissues. So while the heart muscle gets the first choice of fresh oxygen, it can also receive the greatest concentration of toxins that are inhaled in cigarette smoke. These toxins can damage the blood vessels and negatively affect the function of the heart.

The cardiac cycle

The cardiac cycle refers to the process of the heart contracting to transport blood through the heart. It explains the sequence of events that occur during one complete heartbeat.

The chambers of the heart are either filling or emptying of blood. The filling of a chamber is described as the 'diastole phase' and the emptying of a chamber as the 'systole phase'. A single cycle takes about 0.8 seconds and thus the heart beats around 72 times per minute. The four stages of the cycle are:

1 atrial diastole

2 ventricular diastole

3 atrial systole

4 ventricular systole.

During *atrial diastole* the atria are filled with blood that has returned from the body (right atrium) or from the lungs (left atrium). As they fill up with blood, the pressure in the atria rises, forcing blood into the ventricles through the atrio-ventricular valves. This is the *ventricular diastole phase*. The *atrial systole* phase occurs next as the atria contract so that they can fully empty their contents into the ventricles. Because of the increasing volume of blood present, the pressure in the ventricles rises and the atrio-ventricular valves are forced closed. Once full, the ventricles contract and expel blood into the aorta and the pulmonary artery to complete the *ventricular systole phase*.

THE CONDUCTION MECHANISM OF THE HART

Cardiac muscle, unlike skeletal muscle, is able to produce its own nervous impulses to produce contractions. This is referred to as its 'myogenic' property. It has a conduction system that spreads nervous impulses throughout the heart muscle, enabling it to contract. Owing to this myogenic property the human heart, or the heart of any animal, can continue beating if it is removed from the body.

The nervous impulse originates in the sino-atrial node (S-A node) which, as can be seen in Figure 3.12, is positioned towards the top of the heart and close to the entrance of the vena cava. The S-A node is referred to as the pacemaker of the heart as its sets the pace, or frequency, of the heartbeat. The nervous impulse passes across both atria to the atrio-ventricular node (A-V node), which is situated in the septum close to the junction of the atria and the ventricles. The A-V node passes the impulse to the bundle of His, which has two strands, one in each ventricle. The bundle of His branches off into Purkinje fibres, which distribute the nervous impulse to all parts of the ventricles.

CARDIAC OUTPUT

Cardiac output, which is expressed as CO or Q, is the amount of blood pumped out of each ventricle per minute. This is an important measure of the effective functioning of the heart. The measure of cardiac output is particularly important for athletes, as the greater their cardiac output then potentially the greater the volume of oxygen available to the working muscles.

Cardiac output is the product of two other values:

▶ heart rate (HR), which is measured in beats per minute (bpm)

▶ stroke volume, which is the amount of blood that the ventricle pumps out with each heartbeat, and it is measured in millilitres (ml).

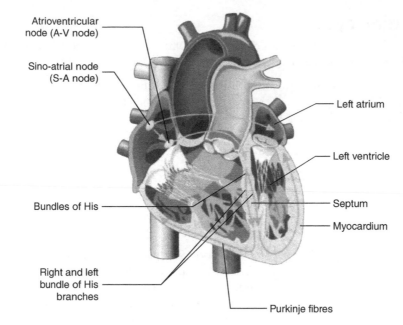

Atrioventricular
node (A-V node)

Sino-atrial node
(S-A node)

Left atrium

Left ventricle

Bundles of His

Septum

Myocardium

Right and left
bundle of His
branches

Purkinje fibres

Figure 3.12 The conduction system of the heart

Cardiac output can be calculated using a simple formula:

$$\text{Cardiac output} = \text{heart rate} \times \text{stroke volume}$$

For example, if we have a heart rate of 72 bpm and a stroke volume of 70 ml, cardiac output would be calculated at 5040 ml/min. This is equivalent to 5 litres, which is close to normal adult blood volume and suggests that the body's total blood supply passes through the heart every minute.

During exercise both the heart rate and the stroke volume increase significantly. Stroke volume can double as the force of ventricular contraction increases, and heart rate can almost triple in frequency. With high-intensity exercise, stroke volume may have risen to 140 ml and heart rate to 180 bpm, resulting in a cardiac output of 25,200 ml/min or roughly 25 L/min.

Key point: Cardiac output

Cardiac output is the amount of blood that leaves each ventricle per minute.

Cardiac output is determined by two variables: heart rate and stroke volume.

Heart rate is the number of times the heart beats per minute.

Stroke volume is the amount of blood pumped from the ventricles with each heartbeat.

BLOOD VESSELS

Blood vessels make up the 'vascular' part of the cardiovascular system; 'vascular' refers to vessels that carry fluids. In this case it refers to the veins, arteries and capillaries that are responsible for transporting blood around the body. Arteries are responsible for taking blood away from the heart and they branch off into successively smaller and smaller arteries before feeding blood into arterioles (little arteries). Arterioles lead blood into the network of capillaries that serve the tissues. Capillaries drain into venules (little veins), which in turn empty blood into veins that return blood to the heart through the venae cavae.

The definition of an artery is that it is a blood vessel taking blood away from the heart, while a vein always returns blood to the heart. Arteries predominantly carry oxygenated blood and veins predominantly carry deoxygenated blood. The exceptions to this are the pulmonary vein and the pulmonary artery, which transport blood between the heart and the lungs. The pulmonary artery is so-called because, although it carries deoxygenated blood, it is taking blood away from the heart. Likewise, the pulmonary vein carries oxygenated blood but it is a blood vessel bringing blood back to the heart.

Capillaries are the tiniest blood vessels and every muscle has an extensive network of capillaries within it. Capillaries provide the interface between blood and the muscle cells and it is through their walls that oxygen is introduced into the muscles and carbon dioxide is removed. Alveoli are also surrounded by a huge network of capillaries to enable them to deliver oxygen into the bloodstream and remove carbon dioxide.

Roughly speaking, the human body contains around 60,000 miles of blood vessels which, if organized into a straight line, would reach around the world three times. This seems almost unbelievable but it illustrates the vastness of the network of capillaries and how tiny some of these blood vessels are in size.

▶ Microscopic structure of blood vessels

Arteries and veins are structured similarly, as can be seen in Figure 3.13. However, arteries have thicker walls as they carry blood under much higher pressure than veins. Arteries and veins both consist of three layers of tissue that surround the hollow space where blood flows. This space in the blood vessels is referred to as the lumen.

The three layers of tissue are:

▶ the inner layer, consisting of a thin lining of cells called the endothelium. These cells form a smooth surface to limit friction between the walls of the blood vessel and the blood.

▶ the middle layer, consisting of smooth muscle and elastic tissue. This allows blood vessels to contract and relax.

▶ the outer layer, consisting of elastic tissue and collagen to give the blood vessels some protection.

▶ Features of arteries

Arteries have thicker, more muscular walls than veins, particularly those arteries close to the heart where the pressure of blood is greatest. Owing to the presence of smooth muscle, arteries have the capacity to contract, which squeezes the artery wall and decreases the size of the lumen. This narrowing of an artery is called vasoconstriction and its expansion is called vasodilation. These two actions influence blood pressure, which in turn is influenced by chemicals, such as nicotine, and hormones that our body produces.

▶ Features of veins

Veins are structurally similar to arteries except that they have thinner walls. The middle layer contains less smooth muscle and the outer layer contains less collagen. Their walls become thicker the closer they are to the heart and thinner towards the capillaries. They have two

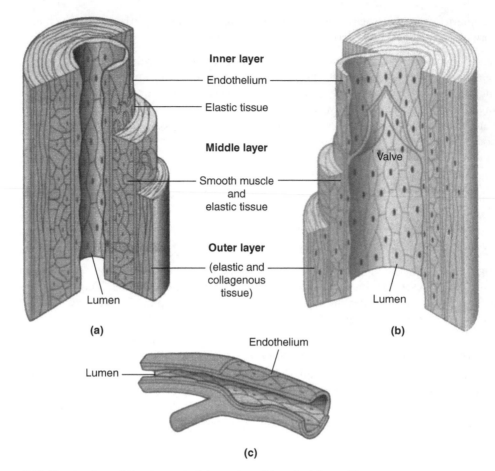

Inner layer
Endothelium
Elastic tissue

Middle layer
Smooth muscle and elastic tissue

Outer layer
(elastic and collagenous tissue)

Lumen

(a)

Valve

Lumen

(b)

Lumen

Endothelium

(c)

Figure 3.13 The structure of blood vessels: (a) an artery, (b) a vein, (c) a capillary

main differences from arteries: first, their lumen is wider; and secondly, some veins contain valves.

These one-way valves are needed to support the return of blood to the heart (venous return) as they prevent the backflow of blood. If you consider the flow of blood from the legs back to the heart, the blood has to return upwards against the force of gravity. The contraction of the heart pushes the blood upwards; however, if one-way valves were not present, the blood would flow back towards the feet every time the heart relaxed between contractions. The valves close as the heart relaxes, allowing the blood to hold its position and assisting its return to the heart.

▶ Features of capillaries

Capillary means 'hair like' and describes the microscopic size of these blood vessels. Some are so tiny that they only have enough space for one red blood cell to pass at a time. They provide the connection between arterioles and venules and are found near almost every cell in the body. The walls of capillaries are so thin that they allow substances to pass through them. Gases can pass through the tiny spaces between the cells as capillary walls are only one cell thick and have spaces between the cells. Their role is to exchange oxygen and carbon dioxide as well as nutrients and waste products. The capillary network is particularly extensive in areas that have a high requirement for oxygen, such as the muscles and liver. Slow twitch muscle fibres have a much more extensive network of capillaries than fast twitch muscle fibres as they rely exclusively on oxygen for energy production.

The flow of blood through capillaries is controlled by pre-capillary sphincters, which are tiny rings of smooth muscle situated where the arteriole meets the capillary. During exercise these pre-capillary sphincters relax to allow more blood to flow into the artery so that gaseous exchange can occur. However, once exercise is over the pre-capillary sphincters contract to reduce blood flow through the capillaries.

Spotlight: Why can I feel a pulse?

The pulse gives us a measure of our heart rate but it is the effect of the heartbeat rather than the actual heartbeat that we are feeling. When the heart beats, blood is ejected into arteries at a high pressure. This causes the lumen of the artery to expand in response to the increase in pressure. Once the wave of pressure has passed, the artery recoils and returns to its starting position.

When we feel the pulse, it is the expansion and recoil of the artery that we are feeling. The pulse is felt when we press an artery against a bone than runs alongside the artery. The two most common arteries to take the pulse from are the radial artery, felt at the wrist, and the carotid artery, felt in the neck. However, we could also take the pulse at the femoral artery, positioned in the groin, or the brachial artery, positioned close to the elbow.

Key point: Blood vessels

There are three types of blood vessel – arteries, veins and capillaries.

Arteries have thick, muscular walls and carry blood away from the heart.

Veins have thinner, less muscular walls but a wider lumen. They carry blood towards the heart.

Capillaries are microscopic blood vessels found in the tissues of the body. They have very thin walls, often only one cell thick, and allow gases, nutrients and fluids to pass through them.

Arteries – **a**way from the heart.

Veins – arri**v**e at the heart.

BLOOD PRESSURE

Blood pressure is described as the pressure that blood exerts on the artery walls. It is dependent on the amount of blood in the artery, which in turn is dependent on cardiac output (the amount of blood leaving the heart). Blood pressure is also affected by the amount of force the artery walls exert on the blood. This force is referred to as peripheral resistance. The contraction of the ventricles introduces a wave of pressure into the arteries that is needed to propel the blood around the arterial system. The pressure of blood will be greater in arteries close to the heart, so it will be under highest pressure in the aorta and then the arteries. Blood pressure drops significantly in the arterioles and is negligible in the capillaries, venules and veins.

Key point: Blood pressure

Blood pressure is the pressure that blood exerts on the artery walls.

Blood pressure is dependent on two factors:

▶ cardiac output – the amount of blood leaving the heart

▶ peripheral resistance – the force that the artery walls exert on the blood.

Increases in either of these factors will increase blood pressure.

When blood pressure is taken two measurements are recorded; for example, a normal blood pressure would be 120/80 or 120 over 80. Both blood pressures would have mmHg (millimetres of mercury) as their units of measurement.

These two measurements reflect the two phases of the heartbeat – the contraction or emptying phase (systole) and the relaxation or filling phase (diastole). The higher reading represents systolic blood pressure, which is the pressure in the arteries during the contraction phase of the heartbeat. The lower reading represents diastolic blood pressure, which is the pressure in the arteries during the relaxation phase of the heartbeat.

Spotlight: What are typical blood pressure readings?

A blood pressure reading of 120/80 is regarded as normal blood pressure. However, a doctor will be concerned about particularly high or particularly low readings.

(American Heart Association, 2015)

Blood pressure category	Systolic measure	Diastolic measure
Normal	Less than 120 mmHg	Less than 80 mmHg
Stage 1 high blood pressure	140–159 mmHg	90–99 mmHg
Stage 2 high blood pressure	160 + mmHg	100 + mmHg
Low blood pressure	Less than 90 mmHg	Less than 60 mmHg

High blood pressure is referred to as 'hypertension', while low blood pressure is referred to as 'hypotension'.

High blood pressure is a concern as it is a symptom of heart disease and a risk factor for a heart attack.

Low blood pressure is also a concern as it can result in dizzy spells or fainting. It can indicate blood loss in a person who has experienced an injury.

There are many factors that influence blood pressure but they will either be the result of changes in blood volume or vasoconstriction/vasodilation. For example, exercise increases blood pressure significantly because it increases cardiac output, which is an increase in blood volume leaving the heart. Periods of emotional stress, smoking cigarettes and a poor diet will all cause vasoconstriction and thus increase blood pressure, while heat and alcohol consumption will cause vasodilation and reduce blood pressure.

Blood pressure will naturally increase with age. This is because the artery walls start to lose their elasticity and thus are less able to vasodilate. This decline in the elasticity of smooth muscle leads to a condition called arteriosclerosis, or hardening of the arteries. It is normal for a person in their 60s or 70s to have a high reading for their blood pressure.

▶ **Venous return**

Because blood pressure is so low in the veins, they have to rely on other mechanisms to ensure that blood returns to the heart. These mechanisms are described as aiding venous return and are essential if cardiac output is to be maintained. Venous return from the lower body is made harder by gravity pushing blood towards the feet. There are six main mechanisms that are utilized to aid venous return.

1 Contraction of smooth muscle in the veins – the peristaltic action of the smooth muscle helps to send blood back up towards the heart.

2 Contraction of skeletal muscle - the muscles that surround veins push on them as they contract. This results in blood being shunted upwards in the veins as the veins are squeezed. This is described as the 'muscle pump'. It is particularly important in the legs where the large muscles contract to help send blood upwards.

3 Non-return valves – the veins contain non-return valves that prevent the backflow of blood during the relaxation phase of the heart.

4 The right atrium – once the right atrium has contracted to send blood into the right ventricle, it relaxes and can help to suck blood up the veins.

5 The diaphragm – when this dome-shaped respiratory muscle contracts and relaxes, it causes a pressure change in the chest that has a suction effect on the blood in the veins below the heart, drawing it upwards.

6 Gravity – veins above the heart, leading from the head and shoulders, are assisted by gravity to return blood the heart.

Spotlight: Why is it important to keep moving after exercise rather than suddenly stopping?

When we are exercising at a moderate to high intensity the heart is working hard to supply the body with blood. Cardiac output is significantly increased from a resting state and if you are running, the majority of this is supplied to the muscles of the legs. The pumping action of skeletal muscles plays a key role in returning blood to the heart and if we were to suddenly stop running, the muscles of the calves and upper leg would suddenly stop acting as the muscle pump. Cardiac output would still be high, sending blood to the legs but we would get blood pooling, or venous pooling, in the legs. The result would be that there would be significantly less blood returning to the heart and cardiac output would be compromised.

This is why we can feel dizzy or light-headed after exercise if we stop suddenly, as all our blood is pooling around our ankles, causing a reduction in blood supply to the brain.

The way to prevent venous pooling is simple. Either keep moving slowly after exercise to ensure the muscle pump keeps working, or lie down on your back and raise your legs. Then gravity will aid venous return and blood supply to the brain will be re-established.

Other systems of the body

The human body consists of 11 systems incorporating the organs of the body. Chapters 2 and 3 have examined the structure and function of five of these systems. It is beyond the scope of this book to examine all 11 systems but this section will briefly summarize the other six systems.

▶ Integumentary system

The integumentary system provides the external covering of the body and consists of the skin, hair and nails, as well as the sweat and oil glands. It is responsible for sensing and regulating body temperature and for detecting sensations of pressure and pain. It also protects the body against infection and eliminates waste products (salts and urea) in perspiration.

▶ Endocrine system

The endocrine system controls body activities by producing hormones. Hormones are described as chemical messengers that tell cells to do specific things. For example, insulin is a hormone that is released from the pancreas and it tells cells in the muscles and liver to open up and allow glucose to flow into them. Its role is to regulate blood sugar levels. The pancreas is one of the endocrine glands, as are the pituitary, thyroid, adrenals, pineal, ovaries (in females) and testes (in males).

All glands secrete hormones to perform specific functions. The adrenal glands release adrenaline when it is perceived that the body is under threat, and this speeds up the heart rate and releases more glucose into the bloodstream. It prepares the body for 'fight or flight' in response to the threat.

▶ Lymphatic system

The lymphatic system works in conjunction with the cardiovascular system, in particular with the capillaries. As blood passes through a capillary, fluid oozes out of the blood into the surrounding tissue to bathe cells. This fluid is called 'interstitial fluid' and it fills the spaces between cells. Blood can only circulate through blood vessels but interstitial fluid circulates around all the cells and carries nutrients, oxygen and water to each individual cell and takes away waste products. Interstitial fluid is described as the medium between cells and the blood.

Some of the fluid that escapes from the capillaries returns to them, but because capillaries have a steady flow of blood going through them it is more difficult for fluid to return. Any excess fluid that cannot return to the capillaries is collected by a second set of blood vessels called lymphatic vessels. Lymphatic vessels take this fluid to lymph nodes where the fluid, or lymph, is cleansed before being returned to the bloodstream via lymphatic ducts.

▶ Digestive system

The digestive system consists of all the organs that food and fluids pass through from the mouth down to the anus. The stomach, liver, small and large intestines are the major organs of the digestive system. The digestive system is responsible for breaking down food both physically and chemically, and then transporting nutrients around the body to where they are assimilated into cells.

▶ Urinary system

The urinary system is responsible for the production, storage and elimination of urine. Urine contains waste products of the body's functions, such as nitrogen produced by the breakdown of proteins. Nitrogen is toxic to the body so it needs to be quickly eliminated. The urinary system consists of the kidneys, ureter, bladder and urethra.

▶ Reproductive system

The reproductive system contains the organs that are needed to produce offspring.

Summary

This chapter has described the two systems by which oxygen and other nutrients are extracted from the external environment and delivered to the tissues of the body. The respiratory system provides the structures to place oxygen in contact with the bloodstream, where it is then transported in blood by the cardiovascular system through a complex network of chambers and tunnels to take it to where it is needed in the body. These are key systems for the sports performer as the ability to perform at certain sports is directly related to the efficiency of these systems and how they work together. Both systems undergo considerable adaptations during exercise that determine the fitness level of the performer and thus the results that they obtain. These adaptations to exercise will be examined in Chapter 4.

Human life is possible due to the interaction of the 11 systems that make up the human organism. These systems each have specific functions but are often reliant on other systems for assistance. For example, the cardiovascular and lymphatic systems work in conjunction to deliver nutrients to cells of the body and ensure that the fluid that leaves the bloodstream is eventually returned to it.

Dig deeper

Online resources

BUPA

www.bupa.co.uk/health-information/directory/t/the-cardiovascular-system

Inner Body

www.innerbody.com/anatomy/respiratory

Live Science

www.livescience.com/22616-respiratory-system.html
www.livescience.com/22486-circulatory-system.html

National Cancer Institute

http://training.seer.cancer.gov/anatomy/cardiovascular

YouTube (films on cardiovascular system)

www.youtube.com/watch?v=AlcAF34MPpU

Books

E.N. Marieb, *The Essentials of Human Anatomy and Physiology*, 8th edn (San Francisco: Pearson Education, 2006).

W.D. McArdle, F.I. Katch and V.L. Katch, *Exercise Physiology: Nutrition, Energy, and Human Performance*, 7th edn (Baltimore, MD: Lippincott, Williams and Wilkins, 2010).

S. Parker, *The Human Body* (London: Dorling Kindersley, 2007).

D. Sewell, P. Watkins and M. Griffin, *Sport and Exercise Science: An Introduction*, 2nd edn (Abingdon: Hodder Arnold, 2012).

G.J. Tortora and B. Derrickson, *Introduction to the Human Body: The essentials of anatomy and physiology*, 7th edn (New York: John Wiley, 2007).

Fact-check

1 What is the name of the firm, cartilaginous tube that takes air from the throat to the lungs?
   a   Pharynx
   b   Larynx
   c   Trachea
   d   Bronchus

2 What is the amount of air inhaled with each breath called?
   a   Residual volume
   b   Tidal volume
   c   Vital capacity
   d   Inspiratory capacity

3 Oxygen makes up what percentage of inhaled air?
   a   78%
   b   17%
   c   4%
   d   21%

4 Which of the following is *not* a function of the blood?
   a   Cleaning and warming air
   b   Transporting oxygen and nutrients
   c   Regulating temperature
   d   Protecting against infection

5 Which of the following components of blood are responsible for clotting?
   a   Plasma
   b   Red blood cells
   c   White blood cells
   d   Platelets

6 Which chamber of the heart is responsible for pumping deoxygenated blood to the lungs?
   a   Right atrium
   b   Right ventricle
   c   Left atrium
   d   Left ventricle

7 Which of the following is the correct definition of cardiac output?
   a   The pressure blood exerts against artery walls
   b   The amount of blood pumped from the heart with each beat
   c   The amount of blood leaving the heart every minute
   d   The number of times the heart beats per minute

8 Which of the following is a correct description of arteries?
   a   A blood vessel leading away from the heart
   b   The smallest of the three types of blood vessel
   c   They have a relatively wide lumen
   d   They carry blood under low pressure

9 Which of the following blood pressure readings would be regarded as 'normal'?

  a 90/60

  b 120/80

  c 140/90

  d 160/100

10 Which of the following does *not* aid venous return?

  a Non-return valves in the veins

  b Resting after exercise

  c Action of the diaphragm

  d Gravity above the heart

The essentials of sports physiology

This chapter will look at how the musculo-skeletal and cardio-respiratory systems respond and adapt to the demands of exercise. There will also be references to the nervous system and the three energy systems, as these play key roles in the functioning of the other systems.

The main focus is on the short-term responses and long-term adaptations of the body's systems to exercise. The short-term responses are the changes that take place during an individual exercise or training session, and these will mainly be referred to as 'responses'. The long-term adaptations are the changes that take place if an exercise or training programme is continued over a prolonged period of time. It can take up to a month to see significant differences in response to training and different adaptations take different lengths of time; long-term adaptations should be considered as changes that occur over a period of 1–3 months of regular training.

Other important physiological concepts, such as fatigue and recovery, will also be examined. Before considering responses and adaptations it is essential to consider the principles of training. These are a set of principles of physiological conditioning that are common to the planning of effective conditioning programmes for sportspeople. They all need to be considered to ensure that the appropriate adaptations are produced in each sportsperson.

Principles of training

For adaptations to occur, factors such as the frequency and length of workouts, the type of training undertaken, as well as its intensity and duration and rest periods, need to be considered. However, there are three other principles of training, often called the additional principles of training, that will have a huge impact on the adaptations the sportsperson experiences. These are the principles of overload, specificity and reversibility.

OVERLOAD

Overload is defined as 'assigning a workout or training regime of greater intensity than the athlete is accustomed to' (Baechle and Earle, 2008, p. 380). Training is the stimulus to adaptation and the individual must train at greater intensities than they are used to with the intention of stressing the body and producing an adaptation. Overload requires the manipulation of the intensity of training with the application being to increase resistance, speed, the number or length of sessions, changing the mode of exercise or the amount of rest. Increased resistance can be applied in a weight-training programme by increasing weights, but in an aerobic endurance or speed-training programme it may involve the use of harnesses, parachutes, weighted jackets or running up hills.

To keep stressing the body in new ways and producing adaptations, the body needs to be continually overloaded and this is referred to as 'progressive overload'. The fitter the individual becomes the more difficult it can be to make additional fitness gains and they have to work at higher intensities to make even tiny gains. A sedentary person who starts training will make huge gains very early on and it is not uncommon for an initially sedentary person to double the amount of weight that they can lift in their first month of training. This can be very motivational for them but it is unlikely that they will ever make such gains so quickly again.

While the aim of overload is to stress the body by working at increasingly higher intensities, this does need to be applied sensitively as too much overload can lead to injury in the short term and overtraining in the long term.

SPECIFICITY

Specificity is defined as 'the method whereby an athlete is trained in a specific manner to produce a specific adaptation or training outcome' (Baechle and Earle, 2008, p. 379). This means that to improve running speed the athlete must run quickly in training. Resistance training exercises must be chosen to target the muscles a body builder wants to develop. As a result, a coach selects exercise or movements that mimic those present in a sport. This can be difficult for a sport such as golf, where the movements are quite complex and are difficult to simulate exactly in the gym environment. Indeed, some weight-training methods, such as fixed-path resistance machines, are misused extensively by athletes because the machines are unable to replicate real-life movements. For example, a bench-press exercise is done with the back firmly supported by a bench, giving the weightlifter something to push against, and this has limited crossover into sporting situations.

Specificity has implications for how components of fitness are tested. For example, aerobic endurance is tested using a 12-minute run test or multi-stage fitness test involving the athlete completing runs of 20 minutes in increasingly fast times. In order to improve performance in these tests it would be necessary to complete these tests in training, which may not be valuable for the actual event the athlete is training for. Therefore, the more closely a test can mimic the actual sporting activity, the more accurately improvements can be monitored.

Resistance training only produces adaptations in the muscle groups being trained and these improvements are only useful in the movements that have been trained for. This is also the case with flexibility training. Resistance training is unlikely to have an effect on aerobic fitness and aerobic training will not have a significant impact on strength because specific exercises produce specific adaptations. This concept of specificity is also referred as 'Specific Adaptations to Imposed Demands', or SAID.

REVERSIBILITY

Reversibility is often referred to as the 'use it or lose' principle because it refers to the rapid loss of physiological adaptations that occur when a training programme is terminated. McArdle, Katch and Katch (2010) state that exercise capacity is reduced within one or two weeks of training cessation and can be lost completely within several months. This is even the case for highly trained athletes who have trained over many years. Reversibility has implications for the design of the yearly training programme for athletes, as rest periods or prolonged periods of inactivity, such as during the off-season, can result in rapid reversals of fitness levels. As a result, most athletes maintain some level of physical activity during off-season periods.

Reversibility also has particular significance for people who train to manage medical conditions, such as osteoporosis or diabetes. Resistance training has a significant positive impact on bone density but only as long as the individual is participating in weight-bearing exercise. When they stop training, any benefits that they have accrued can slowly reverse.

Key point: Principles of training

Overload refers to the principle that to produce adaptations or improvements in fitness an individual needs to work at intensities higher than they are currently used to.

Specificity refers to the principle that any adaptations the body makes are specific to the type of training that has been undertaken.

Reversibility is the 'use it or lose it' principle that while training adaptations can be produced they can quickly be lost if the training stops or continues at a lower intensity.

Short-term responses to training

When exercise commences the systems of the body immediately respond to meet the demands of that exercise. A warm-up is designed to initiate this process and prepare the body for the demands of the exercise that follows. However, a well-designed warm-up programme starts at a low intensity and slowly increase in intensity up to the level that the athlete is expected to work at during the competition or training session. This might involve running at increasingly faster speeds or stretching over greater ranges of movement and at faster speeds to mimic the exercise to follow.

The demands of exercise are predominantly met by responses from the cardiovascular, respiratory, muscular, nervous and energy systems.

CARDIOVASCULAR SYSTEM

As exercise, particularly aerobic exercise, starts there is a significant increase in the demand for energy. These increased energy demands stimulate the need for more oxygen to be delivered to the working muscles.

▶ Increase in heart rate

The demand for more oxygen results in an increase in heart rate to ensure that the working muscles receive adequate amounts of oxygen and nutrients and that waste products from energy production are removed. There may already have been an increase in heart rate before any activity as there is often an 'anticipatory rise' in heart rate produced by thinking about the exercise to come. This is because the anticipation of the training session can lead to the stimulation of the sympathetic nervous system, which releases adrenaline. Adrenaline causes an increase in heart rate, blood pressure and the mobilization of more glucose into the bloodstream in preparation for exercise. It acts as a passive warm-up.

Heart rate increases linearly as the intensity in exercise increases. In trained athletes it can increase by up to three times in the first minute but the actual heart rate response is dependent upon individual characteristics, such as age, genetics and individual fitness level.

▶ Increase in stroke volume

Stroke volume is the amount of blood ejected from the heart with each heartbeat. Stroke volume increases for two reasons: first, exercise increases the amount of blood returning to the heart (venous return) and thus there is more blood available to be pumped from the left ventricle; secondly, the increased adrenaline that has been released prior to exercise and when exercise starts acts on the heart muscle and increases the strength of the contraction of the ventricles, causing a greater emptying of the left ventricle. This dual impact can result in stroke volume doubling from around 70 ml to 140 ml.

The strength of ventricular contraction is increased by the effect of adrenaline but it is also owing to the fibres of the myocardium (heart muscle) becoming more stretched than they are at rest. This more forceful contraction means that the blood is ejected from the left ventricle more forcefully and that the left ventricle empties more fully. The principle that the force of contraction is related to the amount of stretch in the fibres of the muscle walls is called the Frank-Starling mechanism. The emptying of the left ventricle is reliant on the bicuspid valve closing so that blood is forced into the aorta rather than flowing back into the left ventricle.

▶ Increase in cardiac output

Cardiac output, the amount of blood pumped from the heart every minute, is the product of heart rate and stroke volume. Thus if both of these increase, so will cardiac output. As exercise increases in intensity, cardiac output increases until it reaches a plateau. At rest, cardiac output is around 5 litres/minute, and at maximal intensity exercise it can increase fivefold, up to around 25 litres/minute.

▶ Increase in blood pressure

Blood pressure, which is the pressure exerted by blood on the artery walls, increases significantly as the volume of blood ejected by the heart increases, as does the force at which it is ejected. In particular, systolic blood pressure (the pressure blood exerts on the artery walls when the heart pumps) increases significantly. Diastolic blood pressure (which measures the pressure blood exerts on the artery walls during the relaxation phase of the heart) increases slightly in response to the increased amount of blood in the arteries. If arteries have become narrowed, diastolic blood pressure will increase more significantly during exercise.

Blood pressure is dependent on cardiac output and total peripheral resistance. Peripheral resistance is increased if there is the presence of arterial disease. Arterial disease is caused by the laying down of fats and cholesterol in the artery walls, resulting in fatty plaques and a narrowing of the artery space. Resistance to blood flow also increases if the blood becomes increasingly viscous, such as when a person is experiencing dehydration. Healthy blood vessels can dilate to reduce blood pressure as the smooth muscle in their walls relaxes and allows the diameter of the artery lumen to widen. The effect of exercise on blood pressure is the reason that everyone, particularly sedentary older people, should always have their blood pressure taken before taking exercise. Any increase in peripheral resistance puts an increased strain on the heart during exercise and could lead to a heart attack.

Key point: Responses of the cardiovascular system to exercise

- ▶ Increase in heart rate
- ▶ Increase in stroke volume
- ▶ Increase in cardiac output
- ▶ Increase in blood pressure

RESPIRATORY SYSTEM

The respiratory system is primarily responsible for getting oxygen into the body and removing carbon dioxide. As the oxygen demands of exercise increase there will be a significant impact on the respiratory system.

▶ **Increase in breathing rate**

Breathing rate is stimulated by the increased amount of carbon dioxide in the bloodstream, which is present as carbonic acid. The increase in the pH of the blood is detected by chemoreceptors that send messages to the respiratory centre in the brain that controls breathing rate. Breathing rate is increased to expel carbon dioxide and introduce oxygen in its place. Breathing rate increases because of the more rapid and more forceful contractions of the respiratory muscles, the diaphragm and the intercostals.

▶ **Increase in tidal volume**

The amount of air inhaled and exhaled with each breath increases as the depth of breathing increases. At rest, tidal volume is around 0.5 litre but it can increase to 3–4 litres.

▶ **Increase in minute ventilation**

Owing to the increases in rate of breathing and depth of breathing, minute ventilation increases significantly during high-intensity exercise. From a resting measure of 5–6 litre/minute, minute ventilation can rise up to between 150–200 litre/minute when an athlete is working at their maximum possible intensity.

▶ **Decrease in residual volume**

Residual volume is the amount of air left in the lungs after a full exhalation. It is measured at around 1 litre but it can decrease slightly as the athlete forcefully empties their lungs to enable them to subsequently breathe in more air on inhalation.

NEUROMUSCULAR SYSTEM

As exercise starts there is increased blood flow to the muscles and their temperature increases as an effect of increased energy production. The speed and intensity of nervous impulse transmission increases, enabling muscles to contract more rapidly, more frequently and with greater force. This increase in the speed of nervous impulses is another reason why heart rate increases, as nervous impulses are sent to the heart more rapidly and with greater intensity. The main responses of the neuromuscular system are:

▶ increased blood supply and availability of oxygen owing to vasodilation within muscles

▶ redirection of blood flow to working muscles from other organs

▶ increased elasticity of muscles due to the increase in muscle temperature

▶ increases in secretion of synovial fluid in the joints and an enhanced ability of ligaments to lengthen

▶ increased speed and intensity of nervous impulse transmission

▶ increases in the amount of force produced by muscles and faster reaction times

▶ increased recruitment of motor units in response to increases in exercise intensity.

These responses are all initiated by a steady, progressive warm-up and all protect the neuromuscular system from the risk of injury.

ENERGY SYSTEMS

When exercise starts the muscles rely on their stores of adenosine triphosphate (ATP) for energy. As ATP is broken down the concentration of adenosine diphosphate (ADP) rises, and this stimulates the activity of aerobic and anaerobic enzymes and the resynthesis of ATP. Initially ATP is resynthesized by the breakdown of phosphocreatine (PCr) stored in the muscles, but its stores are rapidly depleted, so after around 10 seconds glucose becomes the major source of energy to resynthesize ATP. Initially ATP is produced anaerobically but after around 60 seconds the muscles start to be supplied with more oxygen, and thus ATP can be resynthesized aerobically.

The aerobic energy system takes about three minutes to be able to work at full capacity, as that is how long it takes the body systems to transport large amounts of oxygen to working muscles. The working muscles need to respond by opening up their networks of capillaries to allow the oxygenated blood to fill them. This is why it is important to warm up slowly. If an athlete were to work at too high an intensity too quickly, their muscles would fill up with lactic acid produced by the breakdown of glycogen anaerobically. If the intensity of exercise is slowly raised over a period of 3–5 minutes, the aerobic system has time to respond to the increasing demand of oxygen without building up lactic acid that can seriously impede aerobic performance.

As these body systems respond to exercise over a prolonged period of time, they start to adapt to the stresses imposed on them. However, if the exercise ceases the systems quickly reverse any changes they have made. These changes are called long-term adaptations.

Key point: Responses of the energy systems to exercise

▶ Increase in resynthesis of ATP

▶ Increase in activity of aerobic and anaerobic enzymes

Long-term adaptations to aerobic training

With appropriate training providing the stimulus for adaptation, the body's systems undergo some profound changes. For these changes to occur, overload needs to be consistently applied so that the body's systems are provided with a reason to change. These adaptations are of major importance to sports physiologists who may be planning training programmes for athletes or advising fitness coaches on delivering training programmes. Specificity is a key factor here as the training adaptations need to meet the demands of the activities the athletes will be involved in. This section focuses on the adaptations that occur as a response to aerobic training and predominantly covers the cardiovascular and respiratory systems, as they undergo the most profound changes in response to aerobic training programmes. The next section covers adaptations to strength or anaerobic training and has the muscular and nervous systems as the primary focus. While the cardio-respiratory system undergoes some adaptation to strength training and the muscular and nervous systems show some adaptations to aerobic training, the adaptations are fairly minimal.

ENERGY SYSTEMS ADAPTATIONS

The energy systems are dependent on stores of the substrates (sources of energy) phosphocreatine (PCr), adenosine triphosphate (ATP), glycogen and fat to provide energy for the resynthesis of ATP. Training increases the muscles' capacity to store PCr, ATP and glycogen, although overall fat stores may be decreased as a result of an increased activity level but the body has a plentiful supply of stored fat. Table 4.1 shows the changes in the amount of each substrate stored in skeletal muscle after five months' heavy resistance training.

Table 4.1 Changes in resting concentrations of substrates following five months' heavy resistance training (MacDougall et al., 1977)

Substrate	Pre-training	Post-training	% difference
PCr	17.07	17.94	+5.1%
ATP	5.07	5.97	+17.8%
Glycogen	86.28	113.90	+32%

All values are measured in mM per gram of wet skeletal muscle

These scores are specific to the type of training programme completed; other studies have shown that the trained muscles of sprinters have higher levels of ATP than distance runners.

In order to resynthesize ATP there are key enzymes, such as ATPase, that control the breakdown of glycogen. As an adaptation to training there is an increase in the quantity and activity of these enzymes to support the increase in stored glycogen. There is an increase in the quantity of enzymes to support anaerobic production of energy but the enzymes that support aerobic energy production are increased in quantity to an even greater extent.

Spotlight: What is the lactate threshold and why is it such a big deal to athletes?

You may hear athletes talking about their lactate threshold or their anaerobic threshold. The lactate threshold is described as being the highest intensity that an athlete can work at before lactic acid levels in the blood start to rise rapidly. It is also referred to as OBLA (onset of blood lactic acid).

For example, as an athlete increases the speed of their running, cycling or rowing, the lactic acid levels in their blood rise steadily; however, they will reach an intensity level beyond which the lactate system is activated to resynthesize additional ATP to meet the energy demands of that workload. As a result, the lactic acid levels in the blood start to rise extremely quickly with a potentially detrimental effect on long-term performance.

Lactate threshold is the final point where the athlete is still resethesizing the majority of ATP aerobically; if they increase their workload slightly, they will start to rely more heavily on the lactate system. Thus a good athlete will get to know at what intensity they reach their lactate threshold and remain close to this intensity for the majority of a race.

However, when an athlete trains at high intensities they are able to move their lactate threshold upwards so that it is reached at a higher intensity level or workload. This is referred to as 'lactate tolerance' training and the athlete will work at intensities just below and just above the lactate threshold to gain the training effect of moving their lactate threshold.

This helps to explain the importance and popularity of interval training, which often involves working for a period at intensity levels above the lactate threshold followed by a period of rest at an intensity level well below the lactate threshold.

Training using the aerobic energy systems produces additional adaptations to the aerobic system. Aerobic energy production is reliant on energy-producing parts of cells called mitochondria. It is within the mitochondria in muscles that glucose and fats are broken down by oxygen to provide energy to resynthesize ATP. Carbon dioxide and water are produced as by-products of this aerobic metabolism and are easily taken away from the working muscles.

Mitochondria are described as being like factories where raw products are introduced and undergo a process whereby they become transformed into something different. As demand for the factories' product increases, the owner will need to either build more factories or increase the size of existing ones. Exactly this same process happens to the mitochondria; as the muscles' demands for energy production increases, there is an increase in the quantity and size of mitochondria. The quantity of mitochondria can increase up to 50 per cent after only a few weeks of regular aerobic training (McArdle, Katch and Katch, 2010) and in addition to doubling the quantity of aerobic system enzymes within 5–10 days, muscles become increasing effective at using oxygen as a source of resynthesizing ATP. McArdle, Katch and Katch (2010) identify the number and size of mitochondria as being a limiting factor of an athlete's aerobic fitness rather than the ability of the cardio-respiratory system to supply the muscles with oxygen. It is likely that oxygen is present but the muscles don't have the necessary machinery to be able to use it.

▶ Fat and carbohydrate metabolism

The aerobic energy system breaks down fats and carbohydrates (glycogen) to provide energy to resynthesize ATP. Generally speaking, the muscles rely on the metabolism of fat at lower intensities and carbohydrates at higher intensity, although at all intensities they are metabolizing a mixture of fats and carbohydrates. Fats are predominantly metabolized at low intensities because fat molecules are much larger, more complex structures than carbohydrate molecules and take much longer to be broken down. At low intensities the muscles need a much slower supply of energy to resynthesize ATP so it can rely on the slow, steady flow that fat metabolism provides. At higher intensities the muscles need energy more quickly so they become reliant on the faster supply of energy provided by carbohydrate metabolism.

However, with regular aerobic training the muscles can rely on fat metabolism for more energy at submaximal intensities. They become better at burning fat at higher intensities because of several processes, including an increase in fat-mobilizing and fat-burning enzymes. This is particularly significant for marathon runners or long-distance cyclists and swimmers, because it produces a phenomenon called 'glycogen sparing' whereby the increased fat metabolism results in the glycogen stores not being depleted as quickly. This means that potentially the athlete can continue for longer periods of time before their glycogen stores are depleted. This explains why elite marathon runners never seem to 'hit the wall' that novice marathon runners frequently encounter. This 'hitting the wall' occurs around the 18–20th mile of a marathon when the glycogen stores of the runner are fully depleted and the runner comes to a grinding halt, often combined with wobbly legs and feelings of faintness. The runner usually has to stop and then start off again very slowly as they can rely on their fat stores for the resynthesis of ATP. The advice to all runners is that they need to top up their glycogen stores regularly by drinking sports drinks or eating sweets to avoid the dreaded wall.

CARDIOVASCULAR SYSTEM ADAPTATIONS

▶ Cardiac hypertrophy

Prolonged participation in aerobic-based activities leads to several changes in cardiovascular function. Specifically, during exercise cardiac output increases, while at rest heart rate is reduced and stroke volume has increased. These changes are because of cardiac hypertrophy, or an enlargement of the heart muscle. This is often referred to as 'athlete's heart'; the heart can become up to 25 per cent larger in size. This increase is predominantly because of an enlargement of the ventricles, which are responsible for pumping blood to the lungs and around the body. The walls of the ventricles become thicker, enabling them to pump blood more forcefully, and the chambers themselves become larger, enabling more blood to be ejected with each beat. The increased strength of the heart means that the ventricles can empty more rapidly and more fully.

At rest, stroke volume increases and because the demands of the body at rest are mainly unchanged the heart is able to beat fewer times to meet these demands. While the average resting heart rate of an individual is between 60–80 bpm, it is not unusual to see resting heart rates of between 40–50 bpm, and sometimes lower, in trained athletes. The slower resting heart rate is termed 'bradycardia', and it is the opposite of a high resting heart rate, termed 'tachycardia'. The increase in maximal cardiac output is the result of the increase in stroke volume and results in an increased ability to deliver oxygen, nutrients and hormones around the body.

The increase in potential blood supply from the enlarged heart is supported by an increase in the number of capillaries in the muscles and around the alveoli. This increased capillarization ensures that the oxygen and nutrients can be effectively delivered and that waste products, such as carbon dioxide and lactic acid, can be quickly removed from muscle tissue. The increased capillarization reduces the distance that oxygen has to diffuse from the capillaries to the muscle cells so diffusion can happen more quickly.

It is not clear to what extent cardiac hypertrophy is due to the training effect or to genetics, as it appears that some people have naturally low heart rates to begin with. However, what is clear is that cardiac hypertrophy is not a permanent condition and if aerobic training is not continued, the heart muscle returns to its pre-training size. This illustrates the principle of the reversibility of training.

Plasma volume

Plasma, which is the fluid component of the blood, increases by 12–20 per cent after three to six aerobic training sessions (McArdle, Katch and Katch, 2010) with relatively little increase in the red blood cell count. However, the oxygen-carrying capacity of the blood does increase because the blood has become less viscous and flows through blood vessels with less resistance. This means it can return to the heart more quickly. As well as improving circulation, the increase in plasma results in an increase in stroke volume and an increased ability to regulate temperature. Athletes' bodies use the sweating mechanism to regulate their core temperature and the increase in plasma volume provides more blood to transport heat away from muscles and more water to be potentially released as sweat.

The increase in blood plasma combined with relatively little change in red blood cells can make athletes appear to be relatively anaemic as the concentration of their red blood cells has been reduced. However, rather than negatively impacting on their performance, the reduced viscosity of the blood improves aerobic performance.

Cardiac output

The increase in cardiac output, which means that the heart can supply the working muscles with more blood every minute, is the most significant adaptation of the cardiovascular system to aerobic training. This increase is owing to the increase in stroke volume rather than any increase in maximal heart rate. Resting heart rate decreases with aerobic training and maximal heart rate generally decreases slightly as well, as the larger pump may take more time to contract and relax fully. The impact of this decrease is minimal due to the significant increases in ventricular capacity and the increased stroke volume.

There is a linear relationship between cardiac output and oxygen consumption. Thus the increase in cardiac output means that the athlete is able to work at higher intensities, running, cycling or swimming faster and for prolonged periods of time.

Oxygen extraction

Oxygen extraction is measured by comparing the oxygen content of arterial blood to the oxygen content of venous blood. McArdle, Katch and Katch (2010) reported that oxygen extraction from arterial blood improved by 13 per cent following 55 days of training to approximately 85 per cent of available oxygen. The increased capillarization within muscles provides a greater surface area for oxygen contraction to occur and reduces the distance between capillaries and the muscle cells they are oxygenating.

Blood flow

Following a period of aerobic training there is an increase of blood flow to the working muscles during exercise, and in particular to the aerobic type I muscle fibres. At rest, blood flow is fairly equally distributed to the brain, heart muscle, skeletal muscles, skin, kidneys, liver, stomach and the intestines. However, as exercise intensity increases the blood is redistributed; its flow to the kidneys, liver, heart and stomach/intestines is decreased while more flows to the working skeletal muscles, heart muscle and skin.

Training produces three adaptations that ensure more and more blood flows to working skeletal muscle during exercise:

▶ there is a larger cardiac output that makes more blood available

▶ the diameter of arteries and veins increases and, along with increased capillarization, this provides a larger network to support blood flow to the muscles

▶ there is an increased blood flow from non-active areas, such as the stomach, kidneys and liver, so that in well-trained individuals up to 88 per cent of cardiac output can flow to the working muscles.

The coronary arteries of the heart also increase in diameter and there is increased capillarization to provide more oxygen to fuel the increased demands on the heart. These changes allow it to supply sufficient oxygen to the larger heart muscle and to ensure energy is available for increasingly forceful ejections of blood from the ventricles. The brain is the only organ that does not experience a change of blood flow, as the amount of oxygen needed for its function remains constant and any decreases would lead to feelings of light-headedness and possible fainting.

▶ Blood pressure

During aerobic exercise blood pressure, particularly systolic blood pressure, increases. There is a linear relationship between blood pressure and exercise intensity owing to the increases in stroke volume and hence cardiac output. However, when exercise stops blood pressure falls steadily and can fall to just below its original resting level. Regular exercise decreases systolic and diastolic blood pressure by 6–10 mmHg in both men and women after four to six weeks of regular aerobic exercise (McArdle, Katch and Katch, 2010).

It is unclear why this adaptation occurs and it may be that accompanying changes in nutritional strategy, cessation of smoking, reduced alcohol consumption, lower stress levels and a reduction in weight contribute as much as exercise. Research does show that exercise reduces the activity of the sympathetic nervous system (lowers stress levels) and that it has a positive impact on the health of arteries and reduces the viscosity of blood. These factors act to reduce peripheral resistance from the arteries on the blood. Exercise also improves kidney function, including how effectively the kidneys remove sodium from the blood. Sodium is linked to high blood pressure because it increases the volume of fluid retained in cells. If the kidneys can eliminate more fluid, the volume of fluid in cells is reduced, causing less pressure on the blood vessels that service the cells.

Key point: Summary of adaptations of the cardiovascular system to aerobic training

▶ Cardiac hypertrophy

▶ Decrease in resting heart rate/bradycardia

▶ Increase in stroke volume

▶ Increase in cardiac output

▶ Increase in capillarization

▶ Increase in plasma volume

▶ Decrease in blood viscosity

▶ Increase in extraction of oxygen from arterial blood

▶ Increase in blood flow to skeletal muscle during exercise

▶ Decrease in resting blood pressure

Athletes can become obsessed with their VO_2max, as it is the clearest indication of their aerobic fitness level and directly predicts their aerobic performance.

VO_2max is defined as the maximal amount of oxygen an athlete can take on, transport and utilize. It is a measure of the function of their respiratory system to take on oxygen, their cardiovascular system to transport oxygen, and their muscular system to utilize oxygen.

VO_2max is measured by the amount of oxygen in millilitres that can be utilized by each kilogram of body weight per minute. Its units are $ml/kg^{-1}/min^{-1}$.

Ultimately an athlete's aerobic performance is limited by their weakest system, as they either won't be able to take on as much oxygen as they need or to transport enough oxygen, or their muscles won't be able to use the oxygen that is supplied to them.

A healthy sedentary person may have a VO_2max of around 30–40 $ml/kg^{-1}/min^{-1}$, while elite male rowers, cyclists and runners may have a VO_2max of between 70–80 $ml/kg^{-1}/min^{-1}$. Elite female runners have recorded VO_2max scores of around 60 $ml/kg^{-1}/min^{-1}$.

The highest recorded VO_2max scores are found in elite male cross-country skiers, who record VO_2max scores of over 80 $ml/kg^{-1}/min^{-1}$.

RESPIRATORY SYSTEM ADAPTATIONS

Generally speaking, and in the absence of respiratory disease, breathing does not limit performance in aerobic exercise. However, there are some adaptations in the respiratory system as a response to exercise. The size of the lungs cannot be increased because they are securely housed within the ribcage, which protects them against injury. So the size of the lungs is dictated by the height of the individual, which influences the length of the ribcage, and the circumference of their ribcage. Training cannot change these genetic factors. However, a trained individual shows an increased tidal volume and decreased breathing rate at rest. At both rest and during exercise, this decreased breathing rate results in inspired air staying in the lungs for a longer period of time between breaths. The outcome is an increase in the volume of oxygen extracted from inhaled air. Inspired air contains 21 per cent oxygen and the exhaled air of an untrained individual will still contain around 18 per cent oxygen, in comparison to 14–15 per cent oxygen in the exhaled air of trained individuals (McArdle, Katch and Katch, 2010).

There is also a training effect on respiratory muscles, the diaphragm and intercostal muscles. Prolonged exercise causes these skeletal muscles to become fatigued, a characteristic they share with all other skeletal muscles. The decrease in function of the respiratory muscles means that gases cannot be inhaled and exhaled with such force. However, aerobic exercise improves the endurance of respiratory muscles by up to 16 per cent. Respiratory muscles also become more effective in using oxygen as an energy source and this is supported by an increase in aerobic enzyme levels. Respiratory muscles also increase in strength, allowing them to generate more force for inhalation and exhalation.

These adaptations can increase vital capacity slightly owing to a decrease in residual volume. Residual volume is the amount of air that remains in the lungs following a full exhalation and a trained individual can reduce their residual volume to around 0.9 litre, in comparison to 1 litre in an untrained individual. This means that the functional capacity of their lungs has increased, potentially allowing additional air to be exhaled and inhaled. While the size of the lungs remains constant, their functionality can improve.

Key point: Summary of adaptations of the respiratory system to aerobic training

- ▶ Increase in tidal volume
- ▶ Decrease in breathing rate
- ▶ Increase in extraction of oxygen from inhaled air
- ▶ Increase in strength and efficiency of respiratory muscles
- ▶ Decrease in residual volume
- ▶ Increase in vital capacity
- ▶ Increase in functional capacity

Spotlight: Is it advantageous to train at high altitude?

The higher the altitude reached, the more out of breath you find you become. If you start to run at altitude, you will find yourself in trouble quite quickly. This is because at altitude the air is less dense, meaning there are fewer oxygen molecules per litre of air. The percentage of air that accounts for oxygen, nitrogen and carbon dioxide is identical at sea level and at altitude but the partial pressure of each gas is lower. This reduction in the partial pressure of oxygen in the air means that it is closer to the partial pressure of the oxygen already in the bloodstream and that less oxygen diffuses into the blood. This results in a lower saturation of haemoglobin in the blood and less oxygen being transported to the working muscles, ultimately causing a decrement in performance.

However, the cardiovascular system will adapt by increasing red blood cell count. Training at high altitude is frequently used during training periods by endurance athletes to gain this adaptation because when they return to sea level the increased red blood cell count has a positive effect on endurance performance. For athletes who have lived at altitude during their formative years, this adaptation is fairly permanent; however, for those athletes who spend short periods training at altitude, the adaptation reverses as quickly as it was gained.

While endurance athletes who have not adapted to competing at altitude find their performances declining, the performance of sprinters and jumpers significantly increases. The lower air density found at altitude offers less air resistance to sprinters and jumpers, meaning that they can run faster and jump higher. The 1968 Olympic Games were held at altitude in Mexico City and are famous for the number of records broken by anaerobic athletes, including Bob Beamon smashing the existing long jump record by 55 cm and holding it until Mike Powell beat his record in 1991.

MUSCULAR SYSTEM ADAPTATIONS

Aerobic training can improve the aerobic capacity of muscle for several reasons. Type I slow twitch muscle fibres are generally viewed as being responsible for aerobic endurance exercise and type II fast twitch fibres for anaerobic strength exercise. However, under certain conditions, such as training using intervals of 800 metres, the aerobic capacity of type II fibres can increase and they can contribute more to aerobic energy production (Baechle and Earle, 2008). While long-term aerobic training increases the aerobic capacity of type II muscle fibres, it reduces their ability to metabolize glycogen anaerobically and can reduce the mass of type II fibres (Lemon and Nagle, 1981). This would explain the reluctance of many bodybuilders to engage in any form of aerobic endurance training.

Aerobic endurance training also increases the myoglobin content of muscle and as myoglobin attracts oxygen into muscle cells and transports it, more oxygen is extracted from blood vessels. The increase in myoglobin content is complemented by an increase in the size and quantity of mitochondria and the quantity of aerobic enzymes that ensure that this additional oxygen is used to resynthesize more ATP aerobically. The muscles also increase their stores of glycogen and triglycerides (fats) to be used as fuel (Gollnick, 1982).

Key point: Summary of adaptations of the muscular system to aerobic training

- ▶ Increase in aerobic capacity of type II muscle fibres
- ▶ Increase in myoglobin content of muscles
- ▶ Increase in number and size of mitochondria
- ▶ Increase in quantity of aerobic enzymes
- ▶ Increase in stores of glycogen and triglycerides

Long-term adaptations to anaerobic training

Anaerobic training usually refers to activities such as weight training, circuit training and plyometric drills. Weight training, which encompasses training with free weights, fixed path resistance machines, cable machines or kettle bells, produces different training effects dependent on the number of sets, repetitions and training loads employed. Rather than continually differentiate between the types of training conducted when referring to anaerobic training, the term is used here to mean high-intensity exercise using heavy loads to improve muscular strength, power, hypertrophy (muscle size development) and endurance.

NERVOUS SYSTEM ADAPTATIONS

If you watch a novice engaging in free weights training, you will notice that rather than performing with smooth, efficient movements they tend to move the weights with jerky, poorly coordinated movements. This is because they are experiencing nervous inhibition or poor synchronization of the recruitment of motor units. Motor units, which consist of a nerve and the muscle fibres attached to it, are recruited in response to the load placed on them, and as a load increases more and more motor units are recruited. Muscular strength is increased as the nervous system adapts by improving the coordination of the muscle groups that are contracting (Hoffman, 2014). In the initial stages of training, strength gains can be accrued rapidly as the efficiency of the nervous system in recruiting and synchronizing the firing of motor units increases. An individual starting weight training will find their strength improving quickly as the nervous system undergoes a training effect, whereby it is able to efficiently activate the motor units that are present rather than increase the size and number of motor units.

An untrained individual will find it difficult to recruit fast twitch muscle fibres until adaptations have taken place in the spinal cord to create neural pathways to the motor units. Adams et al. (1993) showed that only 71 per cent of motor units were recruited in untrained individuals when working at maximum intensity. However, the percentage of motor units recruited did increase with training.

MUSCULAR SYSTEM ADAPTATIONS

▶ Muscle size

While early adaptations to strength training are due to neurological adaptations, it is physiological factors that account for further increases in muscular size, strength and power. Changes in muscle size are seen after around six to eight weeks of high-resistance weight training. The cross-sectional area of muscle fibres increases because of the increased protein uptake by muscles that is greater than the loss or damage to protein through training. It is the proteins actin and myosin that are added to muscle fibres with an increased formation of sarcomeres within the fibres (Goldspink et al., 1992). The increase in the quantity of sarcomeres in turn increases the number of myofibrils within a muscle fibre. These additional myofibrils result in an increased diameter of the muscle belly.

High-resistance training creates small tears (micro-tears) in the muscle fibres due to the overload experienced by muscle groups. During the recovery period these fibres are repaired and additional actin and myosin is laid down in the muscles as there is an overcompensation of protein synthesis in the muscles (West et al., 2010). This additional protein synthesis results in increased size, or hypertrophy, and a resulting increase in strength.

Summary of research: Increases in muscle size due to high-intensity resistance training

Staron et al. (1991): Novice female subjects undertook six weeks of high-intensity resistance training and showed increases of 15.6 per cent in the size of type I fibres, 17.3 per cent in the size of type IIa fibres and 28.1 per cent in the size of type IIx fibres.

Campos et al. (2002): A sample of men who had previously trained undertook moderate- to high-intensity resistance training and showed increases of 12.5 per cent in the size of type I fibres, 19.5 per cent in the size of type IIa fibres and 26 per cent in the size of type IIx fibres.

Type I and type II muscle fibres are seen to undergo a hypertrophy effect but it is predominantly type II fibres that show the greatest response to strength training. This training effect is dependent on genetics or the individual's response to the training stimulus and the type of training undertaken. Campos et al. (2002) showed significant increases in the cross-sectional area of skeletal muscle in response training at 9–11 and 3–5 repetitions per set, but not at repetitions of 20–28 per set.

Hypertrophy occurs in subjects undertaking resistance training irrespective of gender and age. Research by Roman et al. (1993) showed that five active, healthy men with an average age of 68 undertook a 12-week period of resistance training at high intensity that resulted in a 13.9 per cent increase in the cross-sectional area of their biceps brachii and a 25 per cent increase in the cross-sectional area of their brachialis. Hypertrophy in their type II muscle fibres increased by 37.2 per cent and there was an increase in hypertrophy of type I fibres but at a much less significant level.

There is no difference between the muscle fibres of men and women and, as Staron et al. showed, women experience hypertrophy in type I and type II muscle fibres. However, because of differences in body composition (women have an additional 10–12 per cent of sex-specific fat), there is a difference in absolute hypertrophy and strength. McArdle, Katch and Katch (2010) summarize several studies by saying that men undergo a greater absolute change in muscle size because they start training at a greater muscle mass but the percentage increase in muscle hypertrophy as a percentage remains very similar between genders.

High-intensity resistance training increases the amount of the contractile proteins, actin and myosin, but it does not produce any increase in capillarization, the number of mitochondria or aerobic enzymes. These factors have no impact on anaerobic performance but they do reduce aerobic endurance performance, as the larger mass of muscle does not experience any increase in the mechanisms for aerobic energy production. It is advisable for athletes who train for strength and hypertrophy to engage in small amounts of aerobic endurance training to maintain or develop capillarization, as capillaries help to remove the waste products of energy production that accumulate in the muscles during training.

Spotlight: Can we increase the number of muscle fibres or just their size?

Hyperplasia is the term used to describe the splitting of a muscle fibre into two fibres, and it is commonly asked whether training can increase the number of fibres that we have. It would appear logical that if a bodybuilder increases in size they are laying down more muscle fibres.

Research conducted using cats that involved them moving a lever loaded with weights to release treats found that their muscle fibre count increased by 9 per cent. Research using rats and mice also showed evidence of hyperplasia. However, this research cannot be generalized to humans as muscle tissue differs significantly between species. For example, cats do not seem to produce hypertrophy so their strength gains are due solely to hyperplasia.

Hyperplasia has only been shown in a couple of studies. Research by McCall et al. (1996) reported that after 12 weeks of intense resistance training the number of muscle fibres in the biceps brachii of 12 male subjects increased. However, it concluded that hyperplasia may occur in humans but only in certain subjects or as a response to a certain type of training.

Most research studies in training-induced hyperplasia have been inconclusive, and the conclusion can be drawn that it is the enlargement of existing muscle fibres that provides the greatest contribution to increases in muscle size.

▶ Fibre type transitions

Research has looked at whether a programme of resistance training can convert type I fibre into type II fibres or conversely whether aerobic training can convert type II fibres into type I fibres. This could be a way of explaining the training effects that occur. However, it appears that the ratio of type I to type II fibres is genetically determined and it is improbable that there is any transition between type I and type II muscle fibres. However, it appears that type IIx can become more oxidative and fatigue-resistant, thus taking on characteristics of type IIa muscle fibres. Staron et al. (1991) reported that after 20 weeks of resistance training virtually all type IIx muscle fibres had started to act like type IIa fibres, and this movement was also observed in subjects involved in endurance training.

Spotlight: DOMS – what causes it?

DOMS, or delayed onset of muscle soreness, is a phenomenon whereby immediately after training at intensities producing overload you will not feel any ill-effects. However, the next morning or after around 24 hours you will feel stiffness in your muscles and all movements become painful, and 48 hours after the training session you will feel even stiffer and in even more pain. By the third day this pain will have started to subside until you train to overload again.

DOMS is caused by both aerobic endurance training and resistance strength training but the increased overload produced by resistance usually causes an increased effect. Often athletes and body builders say that they enjoy DOMS, as it means that they have been working hard and they know that it produces good adaptations.

Why does DOMS occur? First, overload produces micro-tears or damage to the muscles trained. The muscle damage leads to inflammation or pressure changes in the muscle owing to the flow of fluid into the area. This inflammation increases over a period of about 48–72 hours and the inflammation or fluid accumulation means that there is more pressure on the nerves, resulting in pain.

The inflammation and increased blood flow are the body's mechanisms for repairing the damaged muscle tissue, so they are part of the natural process, however unpleasant it may be. DOMS can be reduced using ice baths and ice treatments but these may compromise the quality of recovery.

The degree of muscle soreness is related to the type of training conducted. Eccentric muscle contractions – when a weight is being lowered slowly or in a controlled manner to resist the force of gravity – will produce more muscle soreness than concentric contractions. Bodybuilders use eccentric training to stimulate increased muscle growth, and it involves a partner assisting during the concentric action of the movement and leaving the bodybuilder to slowly complete the eccentric contraction without assistance. Also, downhill running causes greater muscle soreness than level running, as it utilizes eccentric muscle contraction in the quadriceps muscles to decelerate the legs against acceleration due to gravity. These eccentric muscle contractions are much less prevalent in level running.

As the muscle cells heal, they will become stronger and more resistant to damage in the future. DOMS is experienced less frequently as an individual becomes more conditioned. As uncomfortable and painful as it may be, it is worth remembering that DOMS is your friend and will result in training gains as the muscles adapt to the training stresses being imposed on them.

Key point: Summary of muscular system adaptations to anaerobic training

▶ Increase in the cross-sectional area of muscle fibres

▶ Increase in actin and myosin laid down

▶ Increase in muscular hypertrophy

▶ Increase in resistance to fatigue and oxidative properties of type IIx fibres

SKELETAL SYSTEM ADAPTATIONS

The skeletal system consists of the bones and other connective tissue, such as tendons, ligaments, fascia and cartilage, that are impacted on during exercise. Bones in particular come under stress during exercise as forces are transmitted through them, causing them to bend slightly, for example, when walking, running or performing a bench press. Movement is dependent on muscles pulling bones through tendons which are attached at specific sites on the skeleton. The site of attachment between the bone and tendon needs to be strong enough to withstand increasingly high forces.

▶ Bone remodelling

When a force is sent through a bone, the bone bends slightly and this loading causes osteoblasts to migrate to the area where stress is being experienced. Osteoblasts lay additional collagen fibres at the site of the stress and then collagen is coated with calcium to harden it up. As a result, bone diameter and density start to increase as long as stress is applied to a bone. For bones to be remodelled in this way, exercise must be weight-bearing, i.e. forces must be sent through the bones rather than away from the bones. Gym exercises, such as squats, shoulder presses and bench presses, are weight-bearing as the weight is travelling directly down the bone and causing it to bend. Exercises such as bicep curls or lat pulldowns are not weight-bearing as weight is not applied through bones. Walking and running are weight-bearing to a greater extent than cycling or rowing, and swimming is not weight-bearing at all.

However, all exercise is beneficial to a certain extent, as osteoblasts migrate to any site where stress is experienced. All muscle contractions produce stress on a bone where a tendon is attached, and this stress is increased as intensity of training is increased. As a result of the increased osteoblast activity, more bone is laid down and bone strength and density are increased. These adaptations can take up to six months or longer to occur (Chilibeck et al., 1996); however, the processes that produce adaptation are put in place in response to exercise commencing.

Spotlight: Why are women more susceptible to osteoporosis?

Osteoporosis is described as a loss of bone mass that makes an individual susceptible to fractures. Women are particularly prone to fractures as bone development is closely related to the hormone oestrogen, which activates osteoblasts. Osteoporotic fractures are most common in the bones of the hip, spine and wrist.

Bone density in men and women increases up to the age of 35, when peak bone mass is achieved. Bone-building is produced by osteoblasts, which are activated by oestrogen in women and testosterone in men. However, bone density is also influenced by the presence of calcium, vitamin D (needed to absorb calcium in the body), magnesium and phosphorous.

The greater the peak density of bones at the age of 35, the less chance an individual has of developing osteoporosis. This is predominantly genetic, as a woman with a smaller frame will have thinner bones but also an individual's sensitivity to vitamin D is inherited. The risk of developing osteoporosis is also increased by a poor diet, smoking and excessive alcohol consumption.

Post-menopausal women are most at risk of osteoporosis because once a female's periods cease, she produces less oestrogen and thus the stimulus for bone-building is reduced. Testosterone production in men does decrease with age but at nowhere near the rate that oestrogen production falls in post-menopausal women.

While fractures may not be experienced until a female is in her seventies, the mechanisms for bone density reduction have been put in place from the age of 35 and bone density loss is most rapid in the first ten years after the menopause. This explains the popularity of hormone replacement therapy (HRT) as an adjunct to bone density loss.

Specificity is an important concept in training to increase bone strength, as only bones that are loaded respond by laying down new bone and being remodelled. Although each of us has identical bones in our skeletons and they are all the same shape, they are structured in a way that is unique to us. For example, we all walk and run in a slightly different way and this means that bones are loaded in slightly different places and have areas of increased density at different points on the bones. The structure of bones in our skeleton reflects the stresses placed on them by the activities we are engaged in.

▶ Tendons, ligaments and cartilage

Collagen is the primary component of these connective tissues. Tendons and ligaments consist of very tightly packed bundles of collagen which are arranged in a parallel fashion. They are very inelastic and provide strength to transmit muscle contractions in the case of tendons and stability to joints in the case of ligaments. They have very poor blood supply as their requirement for oxygen and nutrients is very low but this can make their repair from injury very slow.

Minchna and Hantman (1989) found that in tendons the diameter of collagen fibre increased, more collagen was laid down and the fibres became increasingly densely packed as a result of increased loading. All these adaptations increase the tendons' ability to withstand forces placed on them. The strength of ligaments can also increase as a result of increased loading, e.g. the knee ligaments in response to running. It is thought that training produces an increase in the thickness of articular cartilage as increased cushioning is needed in joints to withstand the greater forces applied through overload.

Key point: Summary of skeletal system adaptations to anaerobic training
- ▶ Increase in collagen and calcium laid down in bone
- ▶ Increase in bone diameter
- ▶ Increase in bone mass
- ▶ Increase in bone density
- ▶ Increase in collagen laid down in tendons
- ▶ Increase in thickness of articular cartilage

OTHER ADAPTATIONS TO ANAEROBIC TRAINING

Anaerobic resistance training has a positive impact on body composition. Resistance training has been shown to reduce body fat as well as increase muscle mass. Owing to its high-intensity nature, it creates a high energy expenditure during training as well as a high energy expenditure after training, so it can contribute to a daily calorie deficit. Increased muscle mass also increases the daily metabolic rate, which means more calories are consumed at rest in comparison to an individual with a lower muscle mass. These are reasons why resistance training is viewed as offering a positive contribution to training programmes for fat loss.

Anaerobic training can positively influence an individual's flexibility as they may be exposed to ranges of motion that they have not previously experienced. However, resistance training involves a continual shortening of muscles and it is advised that anaerobic training is complemented by flexibility training to avoid any adaptive shortening of muscle groups.

Anaerobic training has relatively little impact on aerobic fitness, except in unconditioned subjects where VO_2max has been shown to rise from between 5–8 per cent (Ratamess, 2008). Circuit training that uses high volumes of work and short rest periods has also been shown to improve VO_2max (Ratamess, 2008).

Key point: Summary of other adaptations to anaerobic training

▶ Positive changes in body composition

▶ Decrease in percentage of body fat

▶ Increase in daily metabolic rate

▶ Increase in range of motion at joints

Factors that influence fatigue

Fatigue is a limiting factor in athletic performance and the delay of fatigue is a major reason why athletes train so hard. In theory, the human body has sufficient fuel supplies to keep it moving for several weeks and muscle fibres will keep contracting for as long as there is fuel and a nervous impulse to stimulate them. So why the body fatigues when it has everything it needs to keep going is puzzling. The answer is that the conditions in which the muscles contract and energy is supplied change and thus fatigue is inevitable. There are six factors that contribute to fatigue during exercise.

▶ Depletion of ATP stores

Fatigue during anaerobic exercise is owing to the depletion of ATP and substrates that resynthesize ATP in the muscles. In sprint events the supplies of ATP and phosphocreatine are depleted within 8–10 seconds, although anaerobic glycolysis can keep the athlete moving at slightly lower intensities. Anaerobic glycolysis produces lactic acid as a by-product and this produces fatigue in the short term.

Stores of glycogen and fat can maintain ATP resynthesis in aerobic exercise for long periods of time without any fatiguing waste products.

▶ Depletion of glycogen stores

The body can only store around 1600 kcal as glycogen (1200 kcal in muscles and 400 kcals in the liver); this can fuel running performance for around 90 minutes to two hours. The length of time glycogen can fuel aerobic exercise does depend on the intensity of the exercise, but once glycogen stores are depleted the muscles are unable to sustain contractions. It is possible for muscles to switch to burning fat for ATP resynthesis but fat is always metabolized in combination with glycogen metabolism.

▶ Accumulation of hydrogen ions

Anaerobic exercise results in lactic acid building up in the muscles and lactic acid is converted into lactate, which causes the disassociation of hydrogen ions. It is this increase in hydrogen ions that produces muscle fatigue and feelings of pain in the muscles. The increase in hydrogen ions causes an increasingly acidic environment in the muscles, which in turn inhibits the action of glycolytic enzymes needed to resynthesize ATP.

▶ **Decreased availability of calcium ions**

Calcium ions are needed to produce muscle contractions as they are released from the sarcoplasmic reticulum to activate the binding sites between action and myosin. During a muscle contraction, calcium binds to troponin and exposes the cross bridge allowing myosin to attach to actin. As phosphocreatine decreases and lactic acid increases, calcium ions accumulate in the sarcoplasmic reticulum and are not released to allow muscular contractions to occur.

▶ **Reduction in acetylcholine**

Acetylcholine is present at the neuro-muscular junction and allows nervous impulses to be transmitted from the nerve into the muscle. However, there is a limited supply of acetylcholine available and as the duration of exercise increases so its availability decreases.

▶ **Dehydration**

Water is lost from the body as a means of thermoregulation. Every muscle contraction produces heat, and heat is transported away from muscles to the skin in the blood. In the skin, blood vessels dilate to increase the surface area through which heat can radiate out of the body. Heat is released as sweat, reducing the water component of blood and fluid available to cells. Dehydration because of fluid loss directly impacts on performance, with 3 per cent fluid loss causing a decrement in aerobic performance of around 15 per cent. This is due in part to the increased viscosity of blood, which reduces the speed of its circulation and thus the availability of oxygen to working muscles. Dehydration affects thermoregulation, and extreme increases in body temperature can lead to collapse and heat stroke.

The effects of fatigue can be minimized by drinking water to prevent dehydration and taking additional glucose in the form of carbohydrate drinks, gels or as food.

The recovery process

Nutrition, rest and sleep are the three key activities for recovery to produce the best adaptations to training. Professional sportspeople often find that their days consist of training, eating to replace energy stores, resting for the remainder of the day to allow recovery to occur and then gaining the optimum amount of sleep to ensure any damage to muscle and other soft tissues is repaired.

Exercise is described as being catabolic, in that it causes structures of the body to be broken down. It means that catabolic hormones, such as cortisol, are released during exercise and these continue to break down the body's structures unless they are replaced by anabolic hormones. Eating and rest switch catabolic processes to anabolic processes. Anabolic processes result in the body's structures being built up again. Hence the importance of nutrition and rest, and also sleep. Sleep has catabolic and anabolic phases, which allows old, weak structures in the body to be broken down and replaced by new, stronger structures. Early phases of sleep are anabolic and later phases are catabolic. It is not unknown for bodybuilders or hypertrophy athletes to get up in the middle of the night and have something to eat to maintain anabolism and minimize the effects of catabolism on their muscle proteins.

Long-term recovery from exercise is reliant on energy stores being replaced but immediate recovery from exercise focuses on returning the body to its pre-exercise oxygen consumption levels and replacing any oxygen debt.

EXCESS POST-EXERCISE OXYGEN CONSUMPTION (EPOC)

It is not uncommon to see a 100 metre runner breathing heavily after completing their race. But why is this, when sprinting is reliant on the ATP–PCr system and oxygen is not needed to produce energy during a 10 or 11 second race? Oxygen is not needed during the race but it is needed after the race to provide energy for the replacement of the muscles' stores of ATP and phosphocreatine and to remove lactic acid. It takes about 4–5 minutes to replace stores of ATP and phosphocreatine, and during this time the sprinter has a raised breathing rate to supply the necessary oxygen.

This is often referred to as the 'oxygen debt' or the amount of oxygen that would have been used if the exercise were to be performed aerobically. However, because oxygen is not available in plentiful supply for the first three minutes of exercise, the energy for ATP resynthesis has been supplied anaerobically. It is now more usually referred to as the excess post-exercise oxygen consumption, or EPOC.

Summary

Knowledge of the responses to exercise and adaptations to exercise are essential for coaches, instructors and teachers who are responsible for improving fitness levels specific to the needs of the people they are working with. The training principles of overload, specificity and reversibility need to be considered at every stage of training and should form the basis of the design of short-term and long-term training schedules.

While this chapter has considered the systems of the body on an individual basis, it is important to stress that they work in conjunction with each other and never in isolation. For example, it is muscles that produce the work to power aerobic endurance activities but they are completely reliant on the cardiovascular and respiratory systems for the delivery of the fuels and nutrients that they need. Likewise for anaerobic strength-based activities, the muscular system is reliant on the nervous system to deliver the appropriate nervous impulses at the right time and at the right rate. Damage to muscles, bones and connective tissue can only be repaired if the cardiovascular system delivers the raw products needed to replace damaged tissue. In turn, the cardiovascular system is reliant on the digestive system to break down foods to liberate glucose, proteins, fats, vitamins and minerals.

Sport and exercise physiology is a vast subject and this chapter is only able to introduce some of the topics that fall within its scope. It is a core concept in all sports science courses as it is central to an understanding of sports performance. It is worth spending time understanding concepts in sports physiology and delving further into the subject through some of the recommended textbooks and online resources.

Dig deeper

Online resources

English Institute of Sport

www.eis2win.co.uk/pages/Physiology.aspx

Exercise physiology glossary

www.felpress.co.uk/Exercise_Physiology_Glossary.24.0.html

International Journal of Sports Physiology and Performance

http://journals.humankinetics.com/IJSPP

Research Gate

www.researchgate.net/journal/1555-0265_International_journal_of_sports_physiology_and_performance

YouTube video resources

www.youtube.com/watch?v=Lo_nuu9KsQU

Books

T.R. Baechle and R.W. Earle, *Essentials of Strength Training and Conditioning*, 3rd edn (Champaign, IL: Human Kinetics, 2008).

J. Hoffman, *Physiological Aspects of Sport Training and Performance* (Champaign, IL: Human Kinetics, 2014).

W.L. Kenney, J.H. Wilmore and D.L. Costill, *Physiology of Sport and Exercise*, 5th edn (Champaign, IL: Human Kinetics, 2012).

W.D. McArdle, F.I. Katch and V.L. Katch, *Exercise Physiology: Nutrition, Energy, and Human Performance*, 7th edn (Baltimore, MD: Lippincott, Williams and Wilkins, 2010).

S.K. Powers and E.T. Howley, *Exercise Physiology: Theory and application to fitness and performance* (New York: McGraw-Hill, 2007).

Fact-check

1 Which of the principles of training means that training must be conducted at greater intensities than an individual is used to?
   a Overload
   b Specificity
   c Reversibility
   d Adaptation

2 Which of the following is *not* a response of the cardiovascular system to exercise?
   a Increased heart rate
   b Increased tidal volume
   c Increased cardiac output
   d Increased blood pressure

3 Aerobic training can increase the number and size of mitochondria in the muscles. What impact will this have on performance?
   a More ATP can be resynthesized
   b More PCr can be stored
   c More aerobic enzymes can be produced
   d More energy can be produced from fat

4 Bradycardia is an adaptation of the cardiovascular system to exercise. What is the definition of bradycardia?
   a Enlargement of the heart muscle
   b Increased number of capillaries
   c Ventricle walls become thicker
   d Slower resting heart rate

5 Aerobic exercise increases plasma volume. Why does this have a positive impact on aerobic performance?
   a Because of the increase in red blood cells
   b Because of the increased ability of blood to extract oxygen
   c Because of the decreased viscosity of blood
   d Because of decreased blood pressure

6 An athlete's VO_2max is a measure of what?
   a Aerobic performance
   b OBLA
   c Recovery rate
   d Lactate threshold

7 Which of the following is an adaptation of the respiratory system to aerobic exercise?
   a Increased residual volume
   b Increased tidal volume
   c Decreased vital capacity
   d Decreased inspiratory capacity

8 Initial increases in the strength of the neuromuscular system are due to what?
  a Increase in muscle size
  b Increase in the amount of energy stored
  c Decrease in nervous inhibition
  d Decrease body fat

9 Which of the following adaptions of the muscular system is *least likely* to occur as a response to anaerobic training?
  a Hypertrophy
  b Hyperplasia
  c Increased actin and myosin
  d Decreased fatigue

10 Which of the following factors is *least likely* to cause fatigue?
  a Depletion of ATP stores
  b Depletion of glycogen stores
  c Depletion of protein stores
  d Depletion of calcium ions

5

The fundamentals of sports psychology

Sports psychology is the application of psychological principles to help us understand the behaviour of people in sporting environments. Anyone who has ever played or watched sport will be aware that people's behaviour can change in sporting environments. The mildest people can suddenly become aggressive and the most confident people can be overcome by doubts and start to make mistakes. Sports psychology is the application of psychological principles to help us understand the behaviour of people in sporting environments.

Sporting environments can place people in stressful situations and cause changes to the way that they think and the way they feel. These changes in thoughts and feelings create a change in the way people behave.

But why? What is happening in people's minds to cause these changes in thoughts, feelings and behaviour? What factors are influencing these changes? This chapter seeks to apply some of the major theories and principles in sports psychology to help us to answer these questions. The chapter focuses on sport but there is a growing body of research into exercise environments as well and some of the theories can be equally applied to people in these environments. Discussion of sports psychology often centres on elite or professional sport but it is relevant to sports performers at all levels – from a five-year-old competing in their first swimming competition to an athlete in an Olympic final. I have used the term 'people' so far but I will mainly refer to 'athletes' or 'sportspeople' although with the intention of including performers at all levels of sport as well as their coaches and other interested parties, such as their parents.

The principles of sports psychology are often used to improve performance, and sport psychologists are becoming increasingly commonplace in modern sport. However, sport psychologists are involved not only to improve performance but also to help athletes enjoy being in sporting environments and to view their experiences as enriching and contributing to their development as a person.

All the information in this chapter is based on scientific research or evidence-based knowledge. Knowledge of psychology is based on scientific research that is presented in peer-reviewed journal articles and the best and most current evidence is presented here. There is much 'popular' psychology about today and there are many 'self-help' books available that are not based on psychology research. This chapter should help you to develop a critical eye for this type of work and provide frameworks to work within, rather than rely on pseudo-scientific work.

While the scope of sports psychology is vast and ever-growing, this chapter will focus on two major areas:

▶ motivation, which seems to be at the centre of all behaviour in sport

▶ arousal, anxiety and associated stress, which seem to affect all sports performers.

We will also look at some other areas of interest or areas where there is currently active research and a growing body of knowledge. Initially, I would like to introduce you to a fascinating area of research that seems to underpin learning and performance in sport and in other aspects of life. The aim is to get you thinking about how the expectations and actions of people, such as coaches, teachers and parents, can influence attitude and thus behaviour.

Fixed or growth mindset?

The first concept I would like to introduce will help you to appreciate one of the most important underlying principles in sport – the importance of 'mindset' as a factor in influencing the extent to which a person can improve their sports performance. But first, answer the following questions.

I believe that those with more natural talent will always be better than me.	YES / NO
It is better to have natural intelligence than to work hard.	YES / NO
I believe there are some things that I will never be any good at.	YES / NO
My success in sport will always be limited by my ability.	YES / NO

If you answered 'Yes' to all or most of the questions, we say you have a 'fixed' mindset; if you answered 'No' to all or most of the questions, we say you have a 'growth' mindset. If you answered 'Yes', we might also say that you are ascribing to the 'talent myth' or the belief that ability rather than willingness to practice is what determines whether we achieve excellence. Why would you spend time and effort working hard to improve if success is determined genetically?

Key idea: Fixed or growth mindset

The fixed mindset encompasses the belief that performance is due to the amount of talent or ability that an individual possesses.

A growth mindset encompasses the belief that skill level and performance are not fixed but are the result of the amount of effort and practice an individual devotes to a task.

One of the major researchers into the influence of mindset is the American psychologist Carol Dweck. She led a team of researchers who investigated intelligence and development in primary school children. She chose a sample of 330 students aged 11–12 and used a questionnaire about ability and talent to split them into two groups: one group who believed that intelligence was most important for success in school (fixed mindset) and one group who believed that intelligence can be developed through effort (growth mindset). She then gave each group a set of 12 tasks, eight of which were straightforward and four of which were very difficult.

Dweck discovered startling differences between the behaviour of the two groups. Students in both groups completed the first eight tasks fairly easily but the students in the fixed mindset group gave up quickly when faced with the four difficult tasks. When questioned they blamed their intelligence for their failure: 'I guess I am not very smart' or 'I'm not good at things like this'. However, the growth mindset group carried on with the difficult tasks for much longer and kept trying different strategies to solve the tasks. Their success rate was much higher than the fixed mindset group, and when asked about why they thought they had failed, they replied that they hadn't failed but had just not found the correct solution yet.

This experiment shows that performance is not solely due to intelligence or motivation but depends on mindset (or attitude) as well. The fixed mindset group's belief that innate intelligence is the most important factor in success meant their performance level had a ceiling. This relates very clearly to ability beliefs in sport, as the fixed mindset view would be that to be successful at sport you need to be naturally gifted or have talent. The growth mindset would suggest that you can always improve at sport if you put enough effort into learning skills and practising them regularly.

This is a sound lesson for both sport and education: if you are willing to put in the effort, you will improve at whatever you are doing. Initial differences in ability are not predictors of how far you might get and what you can achieve – they are merely where you are at the moment. The brain is like a muscle; it develops with hard work and it will change as more time is spent on a task. For example, taxi drivers in London spend hours learning 'the knowledge', having to memorize the street maps of London and work out the quickest routes around the city. As a result they have an enlarged hippocampus because this is the area of the brain responsible for remembering information.

Beliefs about ability often derive from the type of praise that children are given. Mueller and Dweck (1998) carried out an experiment with a sample of 400 11-year-old children who were given a series of puzzles to complete. The children were in three groups, with each group given different types of praise. During the first round of puzzles the first group received praise about their intelligence ('you must be very clever'); the second group received praise about their effort ('you must have worked very hard') and the third group was given no praise. During the second round of puzzles, no praise or feedback was given at all and the performance of each group was assessed. The first group, who had been praised for their intelligence, showed a decline in performance of 15–20 per cent, while the second group, the effort group, improved their performance by 20–25 per cent. The third group showed little change in performance. The experiment shows that while praise is valuable, it is growth- or effort-related praise that is most valuable in a child's development.

Mindset influences how a person approaches learning new tasks or skills. Dweck's work relates to intelligence but she states that it could easily be applied to sporting ability, artistic talent or business skills (Dweck, 2006). Table 5.1 summarizes the influence that Dweck found mindset has on different aspects of learning a new task or skill.

Table 5.1 The influence of fixed and growth mindsets on learning new skills

Factors	Fixed mindset: intelligence remains stable	Growth mindset: intelligence can be developed
Challenges	Avoids challenges	Embraces challenges
Obstacles	Gives up easily	Persists despite any setbacks
Effort	Sees effort as pointless	Sees effort as the key to success
Criticism	Ignores any feedback seen as negative	Encourages and learns from criticism
Success of others	Feels threatened by others' success	Learns from the success of other people

Having learned about fixed and growth mindsets, you will start to see these attitudes in people around you and to understand the limiting effects that the fixed mindset can have. If a person has been taught that their talent is fixed, it can destroy their motivation to push beyond their current level, while if a person thinks they are talented then why would they bother putting in any effort? Mindset attitudes can permeate teams as well, for good and for ill. For example, throughout a sustained period of success Barcelona Football Club was built around smaller players, such as Lionel Messi, Andres Iniesta and Xavi – players who may have been deemed 'too small' by other clubs – yet Barcelona developed a style to incorporate the specific skills of these players, as did the phenomenally successful Spanish national team.

This concept shows the importance of psychology and psychological principles and the role these can play in educating sports coaches and teachers. It is also an example of how sports psychology has applied research from other areas of psychology, social psychology in this case, to develop its own body of knowledge.

Motivation

While beliefs and mindset are important factors in athletic success, possibly the factor that influences athletic success to the greatest extent is motivation. If a sport psychologist were asked why athletes with similar levels of skill and fitness achieve different standards of performance, the psychologist may consider their self-confidence and their ability to deal with the pressure of competition. However, the psychologist may hesitate before then saying that it is something that is difficult to pin down but one athlete just wanted success more than the other. As a result they trained harder, trained in all weathers and sacrificed holidays and nights out to achieve their goal. In competition one athlete just showed more desire and hunger for success and that gave them the edge over the other competitors.

What the psychologist would be talking about is motivation, and it seems to be a dominant factor in our behaviour, underlying the choices and decisions that we make. But while it is easy to identify motivation as an important factor, it is more difficult to explain what motivation is and even more difficult to pinpoint what motivates us. Motivation is not a consistent commodity – some days we feel so motivated that we jump out of bed in the morning and are ready to run through brick walls, while on other days we find it difficult to get out of bed and use every strategy to avoid the onerous tasks we have for that day.

Motivation is so important for coaches and instructors as they seek to get the best out of teams and individuals. The skill of motivating people is often more important than having technical knowledge of a sport. Professional sport shows how complex motivation can be, as it can seem that one of the main incentives for footballers is the amount of money that they are paid. The average wage for a Premiership footballer in 2014 was £2.3 million a year and their weekly wage of around £43,000 was higher than the average annual wage in the UK. But is there a positive relationship between the amount that you pay a player and the amount of effort they put in and the results they achieve? There probably isn't, and if anything a player's performances can decline in response to their wages being increased. Motivation goes much deeper than just rewarding people for their performances and we will now examine what factors do actually motivate a person.

DEFINITIONS OF MOTIVATION

There are many definitions of motivation, most of which encompass our movement into action from a position of inaction. In a classic definition, Sage (1977) describes motivation as: *'the internal mechanisms and external stimuli which arouse and direct behaviour'*. This definition is useful because it asserts that motivation comes from two factors: those within ourselves (internal mechanisms) and those external to ourselves (external stimuli). Motivation can be created by either factor or both; for example, we have the internal desire to win because it makes us feel good about ourselves but we also get praise and recognition for our success. The second part of the definition says that these factors create arousal, i.e. how excited or interested we become, and that this arousal directs our behaviour towards certain tasks and away from others.

More recent definitions tend to view motivation as a process or a series of steps that we take; for example, *'the process that influences the initiation, direction, magnitude, perseverance, continuation and quality of goal-directed behaviour'* (Maehr and Zusho, 2009). This definition shows that motivation goes through stages of initiation and then continuation, which needs perseverance. Like Sage's definition, it mentions 'direction' but also recognizes that the magnitude (size or amount) of effort is important.

Motivation has been explained by a range of theories, the most influential of which are discussed in this chapter, but it is also recognized that during the process of working towards and achieving a goal, motivation factors will change and develop. Huitt (2001) identified that *'the factors that energize behaviour are likely different from the factors that provide for its persistence'*.

Before turning to some of the most important theories of motivation we will look at different viewpoints that are important for our comprehension of the concept of motivation.

Key point: Motivation

Motivation comes from both internal and external sources and influences the direction and amount of effort that we put into achieving a goal.

VIEWS OF MOTIVATION

Our understanding of motivation can be expanded by looking at three different approaches.

▶ Motivation is the result of an individual's personality traits

This 'trait-centred' view proposes that an individual's motivation is the result of the traits or characteristics that make up their personality. Traits are described as relatively stable ways of behaving and encompass features such as competitiveness or sociability. The trait-centred view sees behaviour as the result of an individual's personality, needs and goals (Weinberg and Gould, 2015). This view is popular because it is relatively easy to apply. We may describe someone as being 'highly driven' or having a 'win-at-all-costs' type of personality and this can be seen in their behaviour. Alternately, we may describe someone as the type of person who gives up easily or doesn't see things through. However, this theory struggles to explain how people's behaviour can change over time or in different situations; for example, they may be highly motivated in sports lessons but fall asleep during mathematics!

▶ Motivation is the result of the situation the individual finds themselves in

The 'situation-centred' view adopts the opposite position to the trait-centred view, asserting that situation is the primary influence on an individual's behaviour. 'Situation' would include the other people in that situation as well as the physical environment. The other people may be competitors, fellow participants and the leader. The leader may be a coach or a teacher, and their attitude and behaviour are one of the main determinants in influencing the motivation levels of others. You only need to think about a leader who uses your name and offers you encouragement compared to one who has a less personal approach and relies on criticism rather than praise.

The physical environment can also play a role in motivation. This is the reason that health and fitness club operators spend large amounts of money designing and equipping stunning gym facilities for their members in the hope that they will keep returning to exercise. The use of posters and motivational messages on the walls can also help to give people the boost that they need.

This view has shortcomings, as most gyms would testify; no matter how appealing they make their facilities they still leak members. And sportspeople who are continually criticized by a coach may keep coming back as this criticism can be overridden by their own desire and drive.

▶ **Motivation is the result of the interaction between an individual and their situation**

While there are shortcomings in both the trait and situation approach, considering both factors together can get us closer to an understanding of an individual's motivation. This consideration of a person's personality traits and the situation they find themselves in produces the highest levels of motivation. It is called the 'interactional' approach and is about putting an individual in the right place with the right people. For example, some people prefer solitary sporting activities and some prefer group-based activities. Different people prefer some aerobics teachers or personal trainers to others depending on their personalities.

The message here is that motivation is influenced by a variety of personal and situational factors and that to ensure high levels of motivation in an individual, both factors need to be considered.

Key point: Views of motivation

Motivation can be the result of an individual's personality, the situation they find themselves in or the interaction of both factors.

THEORIES OF MOTIVATION

The three views of motivation are important in understanding different theories of motivation. There are many theories of motivation and I have selected those that are currently being used as a basis for research and that contribute to our understanding of human motivation.

▶ **Achievement motivation**

Achievement motivation is seen as a personality trait whereby people are generally motivated to strive for success, persist when they encounter failure, improve their performances and master skills to help them achieve specific goals. In sport, success or failure is usually judged against the performances of other competitors (externally referenced) and achievement motivation is often considered in relation to our performances against other competitors.

Consider these two situations:

▶ as a tennis professional, would you prefer to be drawn against a player ranked 100 places below you, 100 places above you or a player with a similar ranking?

▶ would you rather take an exam that was very hard, very easy or of moderate difficulty?

You may have made your choice based on the implications of success or failure. For example, if you were beaten by the tennis player ranked 100 places above you, there would be no shame in defeat as it was expected; however, if you did beat them there would be great pride and joy at winning as the value of success would be so high. But if you beat the player ranked 100 places below you, you would only have done what was expected and the value of success would be quite low, although you be pleased to avoid the ignominy of defeat to a lower-ranking opponent. Choosing an opponent of a similar ranking suggests that you like competitive situations where the outcome is uncertain.

How we respond to these situations and the type of opponent that we prefer to compete against are two of the central tenets of achievement motivation theory. These types of theories predominantly consider personality traits, such as competitiveness, that predispose an individual to the need to achieve success. The situation or environment can also be a factor in an individual's need to achieve success. For example, your need to succeed at an exam will be influenced by the consequences of success or failure in that exam. The need for achievement theory is a key theory in achievement motivation.

▶ The need for achievement theory

The need for achievement theory (Atkinson, 1974; McClelland, 1961) was an early theory of motivation and is an interactional theory as it considers that both personality traits and the situation are important to motivation. It also considers three other factors that are predictors of achievement behaviour: resultant tendencies, emotional reactions and achievement behaviour. The basis of this theory is that we have an inherent need to achieve success and a need to avoid failure. Our motivation in any situation is the result of the balance between these needs.

'I do not play to win. I play to fight against the idea of losing.'

Eric Cantona (1966–), French footballer

▶ **Personality factors.** Consider the previous questions about the type of tennis opponent you would like to play or the difficulty of the exam you would like to take. Your choice tells us something about your personality, i.e. whether you would be described as a high or low achiever. High achievers have high motivation to achieve success and low motivation to achieve failure, while low achievers have high motivation to avoid failure and low motivation to achieve success. This is because of the emotions associated with success and failure. Success is likely to bring pride and satisfaction while failure will be accompanied by feelings of shame and low self-worth.

▶ **Situational factors.** Situational factors describe how likely we are to be successful in a specific situation. This based on two factors: the probability of success and the incentive value of success. Probability of success is influenced by the skill level of the opposition and environmental factors, such as whether the competition is at home or away or the weather on the day. Incentive for success is the value of success in that situation. A good example of this is in open competitions such as the FA Cup, where teams from lower leagues are drawn to play against Premiership teams. The probability of success for the lower ranked team is low but the incentive for success is incredibly high and as a result their motivation levels should be very high. Conversely, the probability for success for the Premiership team is very high but the incentive for success is quite low as it something that is expected of them. As a result their motivation levels may be relatively low, so we end up with a team with high skill levels but low motivation playing against a team with low skill levels but high motivation. Often these matches are much closer than they should be and occasionally result in shock results or 'giant-killing'.

▶ **Resultant tendencies.** This describes the tendencies of high and low achievers to favour different types of opponents. High achievers seek out opponents who are close to their skill level so they have roughly a 50:50 chance of winning. They like challenges against others of equal ability rather than playing against competitors who have much higher or much lower skill levels. Low achievers, however, favour opponents who are ranked much higher or much lower as in these situations they have a much greater certainty of success or failure; this is called an ego-protective strategy as they are unlikely to experience the shame and embarrassment of losing to someone much lower ranked than them, and there is no shame in losing to an opponent you are expected to lose to. A situation where there is a 50:50 chance of success is the worst situation for a low achiever as it offers maximum uncertainty and the greatest possibility of demonstrating their lack of competence.

▶ **Emotional reactions.** An individual's emotional reactions consist of the amount of pride and shame they feel at their success or failure. Both high and low achievers want to feel pride and minimize shame but the focus is different for each group. High achievers focus on maximizing pride while low achievers focus on minimizing shame.

▶ **Achievement behaviour.** This relates to how an individual behaves in competitive situations and summarizes the factors that we have explored. The high achiever prefers challenging tasks that are not too hard or too easy and likes situations where their performance is being evaluated. The low achiever prefers difficult or easy tasks where success or failure is more certain and they dislike situations where their performance is being evaluated.

The need for achievement theory is useful in explaining the behaviour of two different personality types in selecting tasks and opponents but it doesn't look specifically at the factors, apart from pride and shame, which may motivate us. We will now look at some specific factors that contribute to the motivation of individuals.

> *'The more difficult the victory, the greater the happiness in winning.'*
> Pelé (1940–), Brazilian footballer

▶ Intrinsic and extrinsic motivation

While types of motivation do not amount to an actual theory, it is necessary to have an understanding of these two types of motivation as they provide a basis for understanding self-determination theory, among other things. In simple terms, motivation can be examined by looking at the sources of rewards available to a successful individual. As Sage's definition said, motivation is the result of internal mechanisms (intrinsic factors) and external stimuli (extrinsic factors). Intrinsic motivation means doing an activity for the satisfaction inherent in the activity (Ryan and Deci, 2000). This would include developing skills, engaging in challenges and becoming involved in new activities for their own sake rather than for some external reward. Extrinsic motivation refers to participating for the rewards that are external to the activity, such as trophies, medals and financial rewards. Extrinsic rewards also include non-tangible rewards such as recognition and praise from other people. There is a third state of motivation, amotivation, which is an absence of intrinsic and extrinsic motivation. Amotivation is present when an individual doesn't know why they are involved in an activity and sees no benefit associated with it. It usually leads to withdrawal from the activity.

It is too simplistic to place an individual's motivation for participation in an activity into purely intrinsic or extrinsic categories. Individuals are often motivated by a mixture of the two so it is best viewed as a scale or continuum, which is a central feature of self-determination theory.

> *'You can motivate by fear, and you can motivate by reward. But both those methods are only temporary. The only lasting thing is self-motivation.'*
> Homer Rice (1927–), American football player and coach

▶ **Self-determination theory**

Self-determination theory (Deci and Ryan, 1985) says that an activity that is self-determined is one chosen by the participant and they will have autonomy or control over their experience. This is in opposition to activities that are forced on an individual where they have little choice in how they are conducted. There is a relationship between intrinsic and extrinsic forms of motivation and the level of self-determination present in an activity. Figure 5.1 shows the self-determination and autonomy continuum, which incorporates amotivation, extrinsic and intrinsic motivation.

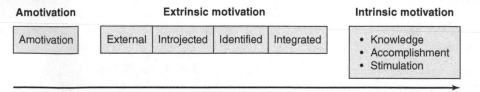

The self-determination and autonomy continuum

Figure 5.1 The relationship between self-determination and autonomy and different types of motivation (adapted from Vallerand and Lozier, 1999, p.142–69)

This figure shows that as you move from left to right along the continuum, the level of self-determination increases. There are four types of extrinsic motivation, each associated with different degrees of self-determination. As an individual moves from the amotivation position towards the intrinsic motivation position, extrinsic and intrinsic motivation become closer in terms of self-determination (Cox, 2012).

Key point: Autonomy

Autonomy is the belief that an individual has control over their own actions and the choices they make.

Deci and Ryan (1991) classified **extrinsic motivation** into four types, rather than regarding it as a single concept:

▶ External regulation: participation brings an external reward rather than being the result of a personal desire to participate, e.g. a trophy or a prize

▶ Introjected regulation: participation is due to a desire to please other people, such as a coach or parent, or to avoid feeling guilty or anxious

▶ Identified regulation: an individual freely chooses to participate in an activity that they don't view as pleasant or interesting but realize it may be important for them in their achievement of another goal

▶ Integrated regulation: an activity is freely chosen and often forms part of an individual's identity. It is still extrinsic motivation (but only just) because it is done for a personal goal rather than for the appeal of the activity.

Intrinsic motivation is motivation that comes from within a person. A person will be motivated for the pure enjoyment of participating in an activity rather than for any form of external reward. These activities are engaged in freely with the individual having full control over how the activity is conducted. Intrinsic motivation is multidimensional in nature and intrinsically motivated activities are conducted to gain knowledge, to progress towards accomplishing things and to experience stimulation (Cox, 2012).

▶ Knowledge: to learn new skills or knowledge about a chosen subject

▶ Accomplishment: to gain mastery over a skill or the pleasure that comes with achieving a goal

▶ Stimulation: the interest and excitement created by an activity.

> ## Key point: Self-determination theory
>
> Based on the research of Deci and Ryan, this theory explains how motivation is developed and how amotivation, extrinsic motivation and intrinsic motivation relate to the concept of autonomy (control over your actions and choices).

▶ Self-determination theory and sport

There are clear applications of self-determination theory to sport, from playing sports that we choose to play, to playing sports because we had to at school or to please our parents who thought they were important. Table 5.2 shows each dimension of the types of motivation and uses an example to show how they apply to sporting contexts.

Table 5.2 Types of motivation and their sporting context

Type of motivation	Amotivation	Extrinsic motivation				Intrinsic motivation
Dimension		External regulation	Introjected regulation	Identified regulation	Integrated regulation	Knowledge Accomplishment Stimulation
Control	External	External	Somewhat external	Somewhat internal	Internal	Internal
Example	'I don't know why I go the gym and I don't like it.'	'I am only doing this because my friend offered me £10.'	'I have to keep going to judo because it would upset my dad if I didn't.'	'I weight train twice a week not because I like it but because it reduces my risk of injury.'	'I love running and the goals that I achieve.'	'I have been learning tennis because learning a new skill excites me and hitting the ball cleanly gives me great pleasure.'

Research conducted using self-determination theory shows that the greater the level of an individual's self-determination, the more positive they feel towards an activity that requires motivation to complete. They show more persistence, expend greater effort, exhibit higher levels of self-esteem (Deci and Ryan, 2000), and show higher levels of sportspersonship (Vallerand and Losier, 1999). All of these factors can lead to an improvement in the individual's performance.

Self-determination theory is a framework that is widely accepted and used in research into motivation in sport.

'I am racing against myself, I want to beat my PB [personal best]. *That's my motivation.'*

Jenny Meadows (1981–) British athlete

▶ Cognitive evaluation theory

Cognitive evaluation theory (Deci and Ryan, 1985) is a subtheory within self-determination theory that is concerned with how external rewards affect intrinsic motivation. Cognitive evaluation theory identifies that intrinsic motivation to complete a task is based on satisfying three human needs, those for:

- ▶ competency, which is similar to self-confidence and is the belief that you are able to succeed at a skill or activity
- ▶ autonomy, which is being independent and having control over your choice of participation in an activity, rather than being influenced by external factors
- ▶ relatedness, which is the need to relate to other people and develop supportive relationships with people you can care for and who care for you.

Social or external factors, such as introducing a financial reward, can interfere with the satisfaction of these needs and decrease intrinsic motivation. This is because the external reward moves control over the activity from an internal source to an external one and when individuals perceive that their behaviour is being controlled by external sources, their intrinsic motivation diminishes. As a result the individual experiences alienation and perhaps a poorer performance (Deci and Ryan, 1991).

Self-determination theory and cognitive evaluation theory both focus on the need of the individual to be an 'origin' and not a 'pawn' (DeCharms and Carpenter, 1968). In order for an athlete to develop intrinsic motivation they must feel that they have input or a voice in making decisions and determining their own behaviour (Cox, 2012).

Key point: Cognitive evaluation theory
This theory explains how extrinsic rewards can impact on an individual's intrinsic motivation.

Case study: Alan's story
I have been mad about football all my life and when I was 11 or 12 I would play football at every break in school and then after school in the park with friends. I played for school teams and a local club. I would often walk miles to a match if my parents couldn't take me. I was very lucky to be spotted by a professional club when I was 14 and when I was 16 I was offered a place at their academy.

This was my dream come true as I was playing football every day and my commitment and effort meant that I improved massively, and when I was 18 years old I was offered my first professional contract. At this time I was earning £1000 a week, which felt like a bonus as I was doing what I had always loved.

I made my first team debut at the age of 19 and started being paid a higher salary, plus bonuses for appearances and goals. I started to enjoy having money and spent it on flash cars and nights out in town. I was really enjoying the adulation that came with being a professional footballer.

Such was my success that when I was 22 I signed for a Premiership club and received a huge signing-on fee as well as incredible weekly wages. I had more money than I knew what to do with, and invested in houses as well as spending money on my family and on fancy holidays.

Unfortunately, I sustained a serious knee injury at the age of 29 and after a year's recovery I found that I had regressed badly and had lost a lot of pace. I was released by my club, and other clubs were unwilling to take a chance on me. I eventually had an offer from a non-league club on a contract of £500 a week but I didn't feel this was worth my while. After a time the offers dried up and I found myself without a club and realized that my football playing days were over.

As I sat at home one Saturday afternoon watching the results come in on television, I realized that I would give everything I have just to be playing football again.

PASSION

The concept of passion, or passion for an activity, is one that has recently become a subject for research by psychologists. Passion is deeply embedded within intrinsic motivation and is defined as: *'a strong inclination toward an activity that people like, that they find important, and in which they invest time and energy'* (Vallerand et al., 2003, p. 756).

Many individuals feel passionate about activities such as their work or sports and because they enjoy it so much it promotes their wellbeing and feelings of satisfaction; however, for some individuals their passion can influence their behaviour so much that their wellbeing and satisfaction are compromised. These two types of passion are described as harmonious passion and obsessive passion.

Harmonious passion is where a person chooses to engage in an activity they like, and while they have positive feelings for the activity they can disengage from it when they choose to. Obsessive passion is where an individual feels compelled to engage in an activity, as they feel that if they disengage from the activity there will be negative consequences and their self-esteem will be reduced. Their involvement in the activity they have passion for can result in conflict with other aspects of their life, such as activities with family and friends. The term 'workaholic' is often applied to an individual experiencing obsessive passion about their work or 'exercise obsessive' to someone obsessively passionate about exercise. These types of individual may prioritize their obsession over activities with family or friends. It could be describe as 'over-motivation'.

Vallerand et al. (2006) identify that harmonious passion results in wellbeing while obsessive passion decreases wellbeing and can increase negative states, such as exhaustion and burnout. Lui, Chen and Yao (2011) found that harmonious passion is linked to creativity and that it can elicit the energy and excitement needed to spark creative processes.

'An athlete is a normal person with the gift of an undying passion to be the best and achieve greatness.'
Amanda Ring

BANDURA'S SELF-EFFICACY THEORY

In this section we examine the relationship between motivation and self-confidence. Self-efficacy is an individual's expectations of success specific to a certain situation, whereas self-confidence relates more to expectation of success across a range of situations. An individual who expects to be successful at a task shows greater levels of willingness to be involved in that task and they persists for longer to achieve it. A person with low self-efficacy is less motivated as they do not think they will be successful and is less likely to persist if their participation results in failure.

Bandura (1977, 1986, 1997) identified six sources of information that affect an individual's self-efficacy. These are shown in Figure 5.2.

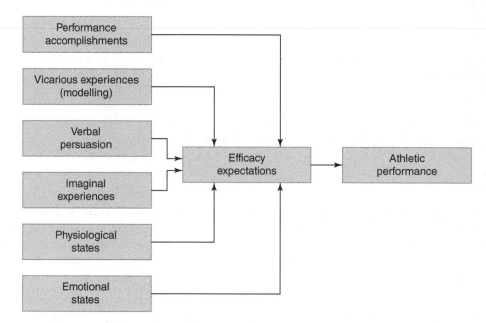

Figure 5.2 Six sources of self-efficacy and how they relate to efficacy expectations and athletic performance (adapted from Feltz, 1984, p.192)

Key point: The relationship between self-efficacy and motivation

Self-efficacy relates to an individual's level of confidence in a specific situation. The greater the individual's self-confidence, the higher their motivation to be involved in a task or activity and the greater the likelihood that they will persist at it.

▶ **Performance accomplishments.** Having previously been successful at an activity is the strongest factor in influencing efficacy expectations (Bandura, 1997) because any self-doubts about success have been removed. Conversely failures, or repeated failures, at a task quickly erode efficacy expectations. For example, as a golfer who has been consistently missing or achieving five-foot putts prepares for their next putt, their mindset will be affected by their previous successes and failures. The effect of success on self-confidence has implications for teachers and coaches as well as performers. It is important for teachers/coaches to ensure when they introduce a new skill that the participants have a high chance of success early in their initial practices. Otherwise repeated failures may lead to them to conclude that they will 'never be able to do this' and quickly withdraw.

▶ **Vicarious experiences.** Vicarious experiences are second-hand experiences or watching someone else being successful at the task that you are about to participate in. This works particularly well if the person you are watching is someone of similar skill and experience level. For example, watching a friend abseiling down a steep cliff may give you the view that 'if they can do it, so can I'. However, if you were to watch the instructor completing the abseil, you may reason that 'just because they can do it doesn't mean that I can'. Vicarious experiences are used by teachers and coaches in the form of demonstrations or modelling to increase participants' self-efficacy, which is needed to learn new skills.

▶ **Verbal persuasion.** Coaches and teachers regularly use persuasive techniques to influence the behaviour of participants. Pep talks in which a coach may say 'I know you can do this as I've seen you do it hundreds of times in practice' may increase efficacy expectations in competition. Verbal persuasion in sport is particularly effective if it comes from someone that the athlete views as credible and knowledgeable. Verbal persuasion can also come from oneself and whether you talk to yourself in a positive or negative way. Also, teammates' belief in you can enhance feelings of self-efficacy (Jackson, Beauchamp and Knapp, 2007).

▶ **Imaginal experiences.** Athletes often use imagery to see themselves performing successfully. This involves closing your eyes and recreating a successful performance in your mind. It is often used by high jumpers before they jump; they can be seen going through the jump mentally as part of their preparation. This process of seeing and feeling yourself performing successfully can boost self-efficacy.

▶ **Physiological states.** This relates to how the body responds to becoming nervous and anxious. You may perceive your increased heart rate, breathing rate and sweating as a sign that you are worried about failing and thus reduce your self-efficacy. Alternatively, these may be viewed in a positive light, as showing that you are ready to perform and you are nervous because the activity presents a challenge to you.

▶ **Emotional states.** Your thoughts and feelings at a particular time, and particularly in relation to a task, have an influence on your self-efficacy. An athlete who is energized and positive is likely to experience high self-efficacy, in contrast to one who was anxious or depressed (Weinberg and Gould, 2015).

These six factors work together to influence efficacy expectations, which are expectations of success, and these impact on athletic performance.

▶ Self-efficacy and sports performance

Studies have consistently shown that higher levels of self-efficacy are associated with higher performance levels (Morris and Keohn, 2004); therefore we can assume that our perception of our ability to perform a task successfully has a real impact on performance. Performance accomplishments are the strongest factor and a reciprocal relationship exists between performance accomplishments and self-efficacy. A successful performance increases self-efficacy, which in turn increases the further likelihood of a successful performance.

> *'A lot of football success is in the mind. You must believe you are the best and then make sure that you are.'*
> Bill Shankly (1913–81), British footballer and manager

DEVELOPING MOTIVATION IN SPORT

These sections have discussed a range of theories of motivation but are only valuable if they can be put to practical use. Theories present information for athletes, coaches and teachers to consider and reflect on. Initially we looked at how the coach needs to consider the individual's personality traits, the situation and the interaction between the two when examining their motivation. The need for achievement theory examined how an individual's achievement behaviour is dependent on whether an individual is motivated primarily to achieve success or avoid failure and the probability and incentive value of success. Extrinsic and intrinsic motivating factors considered the sources of motivation which can be found within or outside the individual, and this was expanded on by self-determination theory. This theory said that the greater the level of intrinsic motivation and control over their activity, the more persistence and effort they expend towards that activity. Persistence and effort are two key behaviours that are seen in motivated individuals. Cognitive evaluation theory supports this view of autonomy and says that motivated athletes need to be originators of behaviour rather than pawns. Finally, self-efficacy theory considers that motivation to participate in an activity is closely related to an individual's confidence of success in that activity. In turn, self-confidence, or self-efficacy, is determined by at least six factors, the most influential of which is performance accomplishments.

Arousal and anxiety

You may be able to identify with the following story. Stephen is a county standard tennis player who has the goal of making it as a professional tennis player. When an important match is coming up, he will be thinking about it for two to three days beforehand and he will start to feel excited. However, as the match gets closer he finds he has butterflies in his stomach and his palms are slightly sweaty. He can't concentrate on his college work and finds it difficult to get to sleep the night before; he also notices his heart is beating faster than normal. About an hour before the competition Stephen finds that he keeps needing to go to the toilet and that he is constantly fidgeting with his tennis racket. He becomes so focused on the match that he doesn't really hear his coach's pep talk. As the match starts he feels intensely focused on the ball and his opponent and barely notices the noise the spectators make.

Stephen is experiencing a state of arousal and has some symptoms of anxiety as well. In simple terms, arousal describes how excited or motivated we become by something. Arousal level can be seen on a continuum, or scale, where the lowest level of arousal would be sleep and the highest level a frenzied state. Your own experiences may include playing in some competitions where you were not interested or motivated at all and other competitions where you were intensely focused and excited. In Stephen's case, he is experiencing high levels of arousal and it is creating physiological and psychological changes.

▶ physiological changes – increased heart rate and increased temperature (sweating palms)

▶ psychological changes – difficulty concentrating on certain tasks and difficulty sleeping.

Stephen may be experiencing worry or anxiety and these thoughts may be affecting his feelings. However, once the match has started he seems to be highly focused, so these feelings seem to work to his benefit. The actual outcome of the match is dependent on a number of factors, not least how his opponent plays. It is not uncommon for sportspeople who are excessively worried to start to make mistakes and poor decisions.

Now we will examine arousal and anxiety as well as stress, which is an associated feeling. We will explore models that help to explain the relationships between arousal and performance and anxiety and performance. Finally we will look at methods that sport psychologists use to control arousal and anxiety levels in the athletes that they are working with.

AROUSAL

There are many definitions of arousal, each one drawing out interesting dimensions of the sensation. Weinberg and Gould (2015) identify that arousal has physiological and psychological dimensions and relates to the intensity of our feelings of motivation towards an activity. Sage (1984) views arousal as a mechanism that produces energy and allows us to recruit the resources needed for the coming activity. As arousal levels increase we do feel more energized and ready to take on a challenge. We can observe athletes, such as weightlifters, getting themselves into a state of high arousal before attempting a lift so that they mobilize the energy needed to perform a heavy lift or overcome any doubts that they can succeed.

Key term: Arousal

Arousal describes how excited and motivated we are about a specific task. It has physiological and psychological dimensions and provides us with the energy needed to complete the task.

THEORIES OF THE AROUSAL–PERFORMANCE RELATIONSHIP

Arousal has an important role in sport and other areas of life. It provides the energy, focus and drive that we need to be successful in an activity; however, being over-aroused can be very uncomfortable, as we may become anxious and experience negative thoughts. Arousal levels are closely linked to performance, as we shall see in the following theories examining the relationship between arousal and performance.

▶ Drive theory

Drive theory is the work of Hull (1943), who proposed that there is a linear relationship between arousal level and performance. As arousal levels increase, so do performance levels, as can be seen in Figure 5.3. A key feature of this theory is that increased arousal levels result in an improvement in performance if the skill is well learned.

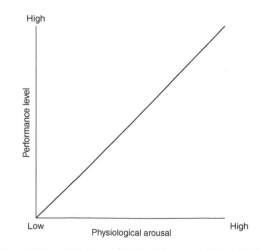

Figure 5.3 Drive theory when skill is well learned (Stafford-Brown and Rea, 2010, p. 63)

But drive theory becomes problematic when we consider the effect of an increase in arousal level on a novice or someone with a low skill level. Increases in arousal for a novice are unlikely to have any effect on performance as the skill is poorly learned and they will not be able to perform beyond their current skill level. If arousal level becomes even higher, it is likely to make their performance worse (McMorris, 2004). This relationship is shown in Figure 5.4.

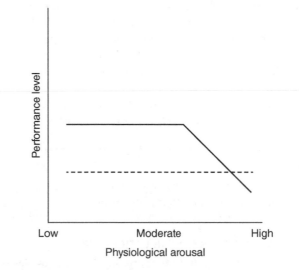

Figure 5.4 Drive theory when skill is poorly learned (McMorris, 2004, p. 247)

Drive theory is able to explain the effect of increased arousal levels on well-learned tasks. It works well when applied to simple or strength-based tasks such as pushing hard or lifting weights, but what about when more complex tasks are performed?

The presence of an audience is a factor that increases the arousal level of most athletes, particularly an audience that is large in size or is making a lot of noise. If you were attempting to perform a complex task, such as putting a golf ball or taking a free kick, the increased arousal level caused by the presence of an audience may not help to improve your performance. Performance at these tasks may be explained better by the another theory, the inverted U hypothesis.

Key point: Drive theory

Drive theory says that increases in arousal will result in improvements in performance.

This effect is most profound when the task is simple and the performer is experienced.

▶ Inverted U hypothesis

The inverted U hypothesis is based on the work of Yerkes and Dodson (1908). They found that the relationship between arousal level and performance was curvilinear, as shown in Figure 5.5, rather than the linear relationship shown by drive theory. The inverted U hypothesis states that as arousal increases so does performance level, up to a point where the arousal state is optimal for the task being performed. Once this point, called the optimal point of arousal or ideal performance state (IPS), has been reached, any further increases in arousal result in a decrement in performance. This seems to make sense, as you may have experienced

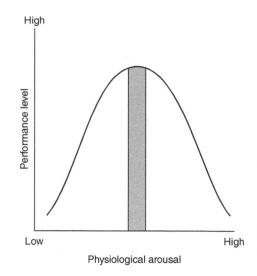

Figure 5.5 The inverted U hypothesis (Stafford-Brown and Rea, 2010, p. 63)

situations where you were under-aroused and not really interested in the activity, and this led to a poor performance; alternatively you may have found that there were occasions when you were too motivated and excited and this led you to make mistakes and perform poorly. Hopefully you have experienced the optimal point of arousal where your arousal level matched the demands of the task; at this point you experience an optimal performance and everything seems to flow easily.

Spotlight: What does it feel like to be at the optimum point of arousal?

The optimal point of arousal is where we should perform to the best of our ability; it is also a comfortable and enjoyable place to be. At this point the athlete is fully immersed in the activity and has feelings of an energized focus. They should be feeling relaxed and confident that they can achieve the tasks that face them. They are mostly free of negative emotions, such as anxiety and anger.

The state is often called 'being in the zone' and is aligned to the concept of 'flow' where an athlete is totally absorbed in the experience of what they are doing. It is a highly enjoyable and productive state.

Key point: Inverted U hypothesis

The inverted U hypothesis says that increases in arousal lead to an improvement in performance but only up to a certain point, called the optimal point of arousal. Once the optimal point of arousal has been reached, any further increases in arousal result in a performance decrement.

The inverted U hypothesis is the mostly widely accepted theory of the arousal–performance relationship (McMorris, 2004) but it does have its shortcomings. Research into this relationship has nearly always used small samples (20–30 subjects) and only a few levels of arousal have been measured, so it would be unlikely that the curve is perfectly symmetrical. Landers and Arent (2006) observe that most research would show an unsymmetrical inverted V rather than the bell-shaped curve shown in diagrams. However, the main problem is that the shape and position of the curve are dependent upon two major factors: the characteristics of the task and the characteristics of the individual.

Task characteristics

Yerkes and Dodson (1908) found that for complex tasks the decrement in performance level was reached earlier than for simple tasks. How does this relate to sports skills? Consider the performance of a goalkeeper in football. They have to perform different skills during a match: one minute they may be trying to save a penalty and the next minute taking a goal kick. When they are facing a penalty, they have to look for subtle clues as the penalty taker runs up to kick the ball, then they have to track the ball and get their body into the right position to enable them to attempt the save. When taking the goal kick, they have to decide where the ball is going and run up to it and kick it as hard as they can. This is a much simpler task than the complexity of saving a penalty. For the penalty kick, the keeper needs to operate at much lower levels of arousal so that they are able to make correct decisions and respond to the information around them; for the goal kick, the perceptual demands are much lower and they can concentrate on getting power into their kick. The arousal levels of most performers need to be adjusted in relation to the nature of the task.

Landers and Arent (2006) refer to fine motor skills and gross motor skills rather than complex and simple skills. Figure 5.6 shows how the inverted U curve would be different for each type of skill. Fine skills, such as putting in golf or playing snooker, require steadiness and muscle activity has to be controlled so arousal levels need to be kept low. Gross motor skills, such as weightlifting, can tolerate higher arousal levels before performance is compromised.

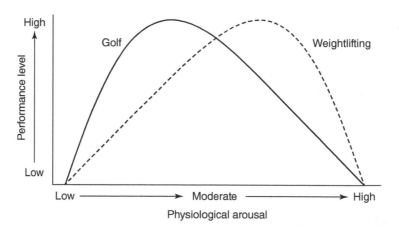

Figure 5.6 Optimal levels of arousal specific to sports (Landers and Arent, in J.M. Williams, 2010, p. 232)

Individual characteristics

The optimal arousal level is specific to the individual completing the skill as well as the skill itself. As McMorris (2004) pointed out, the skill level of the individual influences the effect of the response to changes in arousal level. Low-skilled or novice performers will operate better at low states of arousal, while high-skilled or experienced performers will operate better at high states of arousal. This relationship is shown in Figure 5.7; however, Landers and Arent (2006) identify personality as another key factor in predicting optimal arousal levels for an individual. Introverts, who are characterized as shy and inward-looking, perform better at lower arousal levels. In contrast, extroverts, who are characterized as sociable and outgoing, perform better at higher arousal levels. Introverts also experience higher levels of anxiety and feelings of worry than extroverts and this can disrupt their performance.

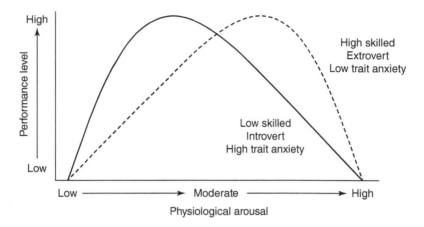

Figure 5.7 Optimal arousal levels specific to different athletes (Landers and Arent, in J.M. Williams, 2010, p. 233)

In summary, the optimal arousal level for any task is dependent upon the type of task and the skill level and personality of the performer. These findings have huge application to sports coaching, especially for coaches of teams who deliver pep talks before a match. The increase in motivation caused by higher arousal levels may not benefit all performers, and particularly in teams where different players have different roles. For example, in a rugby team some players are involved in strength-based tasks, such as pushing in the scrum, rucking and tackling, while others are involved in complex, skilled tasks, such as kicking for position and passing accurately.

Key point: Expansion of the inverted U hypothesis.

The position of the optimal point of arousal is dependent on the type of task (gross or fine skills) and the characteristics of the performer (high- or low-skilled).

▶ Easterbrook's cue utilization theory

Easterbrook's cue utilization theory (1959) is one to be aware of because it helps to explain why changes in arousal level can affect performance level. Cue utilization theory says that as arousal levels increase, attentional focus will narrow. This narrowing of the attention span can result in some important information being missed. For example, a hockey player may attempt a back pass to their keeper and while they can detect the position of the keeper and the opponent who is challenging them, they may not see the opposition forward, who is about to intercept the pass, as their field of vision has narrowed.

Low levels of arousal can have a negative effect on performance because when the individual is under-aroused they may have a wider field of attention and thus pick up too much information. The greater the amount of information available to an individual, the harder it can become to make a decision, as there is more information available that is irrelevant to the decision. At the optimal point of arousal the sports performer is focusing on the correct information and has not cut out additional important information.

Spotlight: Why can high levels of arousal negatively affect sports performance?

Apart from changes in attentional focus, increased arousal levels are associated with physical changes, such as increases in muscle tension, reduced coordination and increased fatigue. Stress and anxiety are related to high arousal levels and when an individual is stressed you often see that their shoulders are hunched up and they have tension in their facial expressions. You may have experienced the muscular aches and pains that come from having experienced high arousal levels over a long period of time and how tired being in this heightened state can make you.

It is difficult to perform well at most sports when you have tension in your muscles as it interrupts the coordination of your movements. Once you are able to relax it becomes easier to perform sports skills, particularly complex skills.

▶ **Catastrophe theory**

Catastrophe theory (Fazey and Hardy, 1988) presents another adaptation to the inverted U hypothesis. This theory also contends that the curve will not be curvilinear in shape. Figure 5.8 shows that once arousal levels have gone just past their optimal point, any further increase in arousal level leads to a sudden drop in performance level. This is in contrast to the steady fall-off of performance shown by the inverted U hypothesis. It is associated with an athlete worrying excessively about their performance. The point where performance levels drop is described as 'the point of catastrophe' and is indicated with an arrow in Figure 5.8.

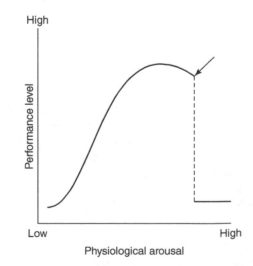

Figure 5.8 Catastrophe theory showing the point of catastrophe (Stafford-Brown and Rea, 2010, p. 63)

This theory helps to explain the phenomenon of 'choking'. Choking is characterized by an athlete suddenly starting to make major errors and being unable to control their performance. It can be seen when tennis players start missing the back line by metres, golfers start hitting wild shots and missing easy putts, or cricketers are unable to make contact with the ball. Usually, the athlete has too much muscle tension so they have lost their coordination. Also their attentional focus may have narrowed excessively. From being in a position where they were performing well, they are now playing like a novice.

> 'Choking is being in a position to win, and then experiencing some critical failure of nerve or spirit. That never happened to me. And I can't help but think it was because I was never afraid to lose.'
>
> Pete Sampras (1971–), American tennis player

Key point: Catastrophe theory

Catastrophe theory states that once the optimal point of arousal has been reached, any further increases in arousal may lead to a drastic decrement in performance.

These are a selection of the main theories that help to explain the arousal–performance relationship. Clearly arousal levels influence performance, but as the theories show this relationship is complex and the characteristics of the individual performer and the task need to be considered when identifying where the optimal point of arousal may fall.

ANXIETY

Anxiety is an emotion that is the focus of much research by sport psychologists because of the impact on sports performance. Anxiety, which is closely associated with high levels of arousal, is characterized by feelings of worry, which is one of the causes of performance decrement in athletes. Anxiety has often been viewed as a negative mood state because of the symptoms it produces; however, some theories show that anxiety can have positive effects as well. It can cause us to focus on an activity and not become complacent about our performance.

▶ Trait and state anxiety

There are different types of anxiety and these are described as trait anxiety and state anxiety. Consider, for instance, a person who worries about a lot of situations and finds things such as taking an exam, speaking in public and sporting competitions cause anxiety. We would say that this person has high trait anxiety, meaning that they have anxiety as a personality trait. A trait is a relatively stable way of thinking and behaving. A person who does not usually worry about things would have low trait anxiety. They might be described as laid-back or generally relaxed.

However, there are certain situations that cause an anxiety response in almost everyone. For example, being faced by a snake, tiger or large spider induces feelings of anxiety in most people, and rightly so as our survival is in jeopardy. This is called state anxiety and describes our anxiety response to a certain situation. So if we were to progress from playing sport at school level to county level and then on to national and international level, we may find each level makes us more anxious than the previous one. We have experienced an increased state anxiety response.

State anxiety is influenced by trait anxiety, as an individual who has higher levels of trait anxiety is likely to experience an increased state anxiety response. Martens (1977) points out that high levels of trait anxiety are a response to the threat of being evaluated by other people in a negative way. As an athlete with high trait anxiety performs at increasingly higher levels, they may feel increasingly insecure as their performances are being evaluated by more and more people and they are expected to perform well. We could assume that the double Olympic champion Usain Bolt has low levels of trait anxiety as he seems to be incredibly relaxed at every championships where he competes. He is often seen joking with officials and other competitors, in contrast to other athletes who seem tense and uncomfortable in the high-pressure situation.

Key point: Trait and state anxiety

Trait anxiety describes anxiety as aspect of an individual's personality. An individual with high trait anxiety finds that a wide range of situations cause an anxiety response.

State anxiety describes the anxiety response of an individual to a specific situation.

Spotlight: What about stress?

Stress is closely aligned to both arousal and anxiety but it differs slightly from both. When our arousal levels increase, our body experiences increased stress. An individual's arousal levels rise in response to completing a task or being involved in an activity, and the individual makes a judgement as to whether they feel they have the resources, such as energy and skill, to meet this challenge. Stress occurs when the individual perceives that they don't have the physical and psychological resources necessary to meet the challenge and that there will be important consequences in the success or failure of the activity. As stress levels increase, anxiety may also be experienced in its cognitive and somatic forms.

Selye (1983) viewed stress as an emotion that accompanies arousal. However, he saw stress as having positive and negative aspects. He labelled positive stress *eustress* and negative stress *distress*. Eustress brings excitement and stimulation and gives us the energy and focus to move into action and get things done. For example, sporting situations can be exciting and offer us a pleasurable form of stress as our skills and abilities are put under pressure. Some sportspeople, such as rock climbers or skiers, actually seek out stressful situations as they enjoy the experience. Eustress is positive because without any stress in our lives most of us would become psychologically stale or bored.

Negative stress, distress, can feel unpleasant as it causes anxiety and worry. Symptoms of stress include an increased heart rate and breathing rate, tightness in the chest and difficulty in concentrating. These can all contribute to disruptions in our performance. In the long term, continual exposure to stress can lead to conditions such as burnout and mental breakdown. It is associated with feelings of depression and seems to be prevalent in international cricketers in particular; Jonathon Trott and Marcus Trescothick have both had to have time away from cricket to deal with stress-related problems.

The point where eustress becomes distress is different for each individual and is influenced by our personality type and whether we perceive the situations we find ourselves in as stressful.

▶ Multidimensional anxiety theory

The emotion of anxiety has an effect on an individual's thoughts (cognitive anxiety) as well as their feelings (somatic anxiety) and this is why anxiety is described as multidimensional. The view that anxiety has both cognitive and somatic components is the basis of multidimensional anxiety theory, or MAT (Martens et al., 1990a), which presents the relationship between competitive state anxiety and performance. Martens et al. proposed that cognitive state anxiety, somatic state anxiety and self-confidence all have a different relationship with performance.

Cognitive state anxiety describes the mental component of anxiety (Cox, 2012) and usually involves concerns such as the fear of failure, or being made to look foolish and incompetent in front of people who are evaluating you. Somatic state anxiety describes the physical response to anxiety, such as an increased heart rate, breathing rate, muscular tension and an increased desire to go to the toilet. These two components, along with self-confidence, make up the dimensions of anxiety. If an athlete is experiencing high level of fear of failure and insecurity, it is likely that their self-confidence (expectations of success) will be eroded. However, if they feel they are likely to be successful and are positive about their performance, their self-confidence should be high. Cognitive state anxiety and self-confidence are closely related for these reasons.

Key point: Cognitive and somatic anxiety

Cognitive anxiety describes the effect that anxiety has on an individual's thoughts, while somatic anxiety describes its physical effects.

The relationships between dimensions of anxiety and performance

Figure 5.9 shows that performance is predicted to decline as cognitive state anxiety increases. This shows a negative linear relationship.

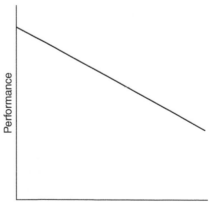

Figure 5.9 The relationship between cognitive state anxiety and performance (Tod et al., 2010, p. 77)

Figure 5.10 shows that performance is predicted to improve as somatic state anxiety increases but only up to a certain point, after which it starts to decline. It shares an inverted U relationship with Yerkes and Dodson's (1908) arousal–performance relationship.

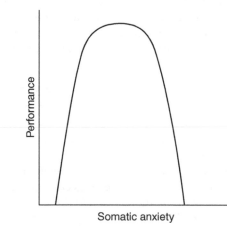

Figure 5.10 The relationship between somatic state anxiety and performance (Tod et al., 2010, p. 77)

Figure 5.11 shows that performance is predicted to increase as self-confidence increases. This shows a positive linear relationship.

Figure 5.11 The relationship between self-confidence and performance (Tod et al., 2010, p. 77)

Multidimensional anxiety theory has been used in many research studies but it has also come in for a lot of criticism. Studies have shown that the cognitive and somatic aspects of state anxiety do predict performance differently but the precise relationships as presented in MAT are not fully supported (Arent and Landers, 2003). One major criticism is that the model appears to ignore any relationship between cognitive state and somatic state anxiety. This is problematic because thoughts (cognitive dimension) always impact on feelings (somatic dimension) and the two are intimately related. The second criticism is that increases in cognitive state anxiety do not always result in a decline in performance. What is important is how the individual interprets anxiety rather than the amount or type of anxiety. This latter point leads us to reversal theory (Kerr, 1985, 1997).

Key point: Multidimensional anxiety theory (MAT)

MAT proposes that cognitive anxiety, somatic anxiety and self-confidence each have a different relationship with performance.

▶ Reversal theory

Although reversal theory is strictly an arousal–performance theory, it increases our understanding of anxiety and its influence on performance. Reversal theory presents the view that the effect arousal has on performance is dependent on how high arousal levels are interpreted. In the moments before an important race or match an athlete may be experiencing high levels of arousal and they could interpret these feelings as either pleasurable excitement or unpleasant anxiety. This interpretation is influenced by an individual's personality and the level of arousal they are comfortable with.

Reversal theory predicts that if athletes interpret their high arousal levels as pleasurable excitement rather than unpleasant anxiety, it can improve their performance. In practice, the athlete may say, 'My feelings of anxiety are telling me that this race is important and I am physically and psychologically ready for it'. This is in contrast to them saying, 'My anxiety levels are high because I am terrified of failing'. If interpreted positively, high anxiety levels can be facilitative to performance rather than debilitative.

Key term: Reversal theory

Reversal theory says that how an athlete interprets their arousal and anxiety will have an impact on their performance.

▶ Measuring anxiety

For sports psychologists, measuring anxiety is important as a means of identifying the impact anxiety is having on performance and also who may need a psychological intervention to help control their anxiety and arousal levels. Anxiety is usually measured using a self-reporting scale where a participant rates their feelings against a number of items. Different tests are used to measure levels of trait and state anxiety. There are many different tests available but the two most prevalently used are the Competitive State Anxiety Inventory-2 (CSAI-2), which measures state anxiety, and the Sport Anxiety Scale-2 (SAS-2), which measures trait anxiety.

CSAI-2 (Martens et al., 1990b) asks participants to rate themselves on 27 statements that relate to cognitive state and somatic state dimensions of anxiety as well as self-confidence. Individual scores are then allocated to each of the three dimensions and the participant can assess whether their level of each dimension is at a desirable level. MAT suggests the preferable profile is one where cognitive state anxiety is low, somatic state anxiety is moderate and self-confidence is high. Table 5.3 presents some of the items found in the CSAI-2. The test is administered before a competition and the participant is asked to rate their feelings about the event.

Table 5.3 A sample of items from CSAI-2 (Martens et al., 1990b)

Statement	Not at all	Somewhat	Moderately so	Very much so
I am concerned about this competition	1	2	3	4
I feel nervous	1	2	3	4
I feel at ease	1	2	3	4
I have self-doubts	1	2	3	4
I feel jittery	1	2	3	4
I feel comfortable	1	2	3	4

SAS-2 (Smith et al., 2006) measures trait anxiety by using a self-reporting scale in a similar way to the CSAI-2 measure of state anxiety. However, this time the questionnaire can be administered at any time and asks how the athlete generally feels before or during competition. A selection of items from SAS-2 are shown in Table 5.4.

Table 5.4 A sample of items from SAS-2 (Smith et al., 2006)

Statement	Not at all	Somewhat	Moderately so	Very much so
My body feels tense	1	2	3	4
I worry that I will play badly	1	2	3	4
I cannot think clearly during the game	1	2	3	4
My stomach feels upset	1	2	3	4
It is hard to concentrate on the game	1	2	3	4
I worry that I will let others down	1	2	3	4

The full tests can be found online by entering CSAI-2 or SAS-2 into an internet search engine.

The use of self-reporting scales can be an effective method of gathering information; however, it does rely on the honesty of the participant, who may answer the questions in a way that they feel will make them look good rather than answering them honestly. Also, the scales are only as effective as the theory behind them. For example, several weaknesses of MAT have been previously discussed and CSAI-2 is based on MAT; thus if the theory is unconvincing, the results obtained may also be of limited value.

▶ Perfectionism in sports performers

Perfectionism in sport is exhibited by performers who are searching for the perfect performance rather than just success or excellence. Perfectionism is multidimensional in nature but can be reduced to two types: functional and dysfunctional perfectionism (Sager and Stoeber, 2009). Functional perfectionism is positive in nature and a functional perfectionist sets high personal standards, desires organization in their life, is persistent in working towards their goals and strives for the perfect performance. Dysfunctional perfectionism is negative in nature and a dysfunctional perfectionist is concerned about the mistakes they make, parental expectations and parental criticism. They also have self-doubts about their actions and feel other people have high expectations of them (Anshel and Sutarso, 2010).

Perfectionism is linked to anxiety because dysfunctional pessimists show higher levels of cognitive state and somatic state anxiety (Stoeber et al., 2007). A dysfunctional perfectionist experiences and is motivated by a fear of failure and the fear of experiencing shame and embarrassment. They also show increased anger and react angrily to their own and other people's mistakes (Vallance, Dunn and Dunn, 2006). In contrast, a functional perfectionist shows lower levels of state anxiety and higher levels of self-confidence (Stoeber et al., 2007).

While functional perfectionism can contribute to a commitment to high performance standards, dysfunctional perfectionism needs to be addressed by the coach and the athlete. This can be done if the athlete breaks the link between their performance and their self-worth and reduces the irrational sense of importance that they place on being successful (Hill, Hall and Appleton, 2010).

CONTROLLING AROUSAL AND ANXIETY LEVELS

Arousal–performance relationships, such as the inverted U hypothesis, show that high levels of arousal can result in a decrement in performance, and multidimensional anxiety theory shows that high levels of cognitive and somatic anxiety can negatively impact on performance. Therefore the control of arousal and anxiety levels is an important skill for sports performers to develop. Sport psychologists can teach different techniques to manage arousal and anxiety and they adopt the approach that different techniques are effective for different performers. There are many techniques available and I have chosen three techniques to examine: relaxation techniques, imagery and systematic desensitization.

▶ Relaxation techniques

Relaxation skills are beneficial for performers who experience high levels of arousal and anxiety to the extent that these are damaging their performance, or performers who play a sport, such as golf or archery, where low levels of arousal are beneficial. Progressive muscular relaxation (PMR), initially developed by Jacobsen (1938), is an important technique that involves tensing and relaxing specific muscles. It is done using a recorded script that takes the individual through the muscles of the body, usually starting at the hands and moving up to the arms and shoulders, into the face and neck, down the back to the buttocks and finally to the legs and feet.

The individual learns the difference between tension and relaxation and experiences an increased effect each time that they practise the programme. They can also become relaxed much more quickly. The aim is for the individual to understand what tension and relaxation feel like so that when they become tense they can quickly relax their muscles, even on the sports field. While total relaxation may not be desirable in sport, the athlete can learn to achieve a lower arousal level or to lower their anxiety levels when involved in a competition. They usually learn to use a trigger, such as clenching their fists and then relaxing, to induce relaxation throughout the body. For example, a golfer at the first tee of an important event may be tense and worried but if they can take a few moments to relax before they play their shot, they may get rid of some of the muscle tension that could cause a poor outcome.

PMR is particularly effective for individuals with high somatic anxiety because as they relax their body, their mind will become more relaxed as well. However, for individuals with high cognitive anxiety, imagery or mental relaxation techniques may be more effective.

Key point: Relaxation skills

Relaxation skills are used to lower levels of arousal and anxiety and involve the tensing of muscle groups followed by their relaxation.

▶ Imagery

Imagery, also referred to as visualization, involves the development of images in your mind and can be used for a range of purposes. Two uses of imagery – for relaxation and mental rehearsal – are covered here.

To use imagery for relaxation you need to think of a specific time or situation when you felt really relaxed and recreate this situation in your mind. It is often related to a place or activity; for example, somewhere you went on holiday or a special place that you go to so that you can get away from everything. When you recreate the situation, you need to engage all your senses so that you see the place where you are, hear any sounds specific to the place (e.g. the sound of the sea or a river) and feel any related sensations, such as the heat of the sun. You can also include specific smells and anything your body is touching.

The aim is that as your mind becomes more and more relaxed, the feelings of relaxation spread to the body and the whole body becomes relaxed. Then when anxiety or arousal levels become too high, you can quickly recreate this relaxing place and the feelings of relaxation will replace the tension in the mind and the body.

Mental rehearsal is the mental recreation of the feelings of performing sports skills. Before an event the athlete may recreate the race or the skills they will perform exactly. We can often see high jumpers, golfers and penalty kickers in rugby going through their performance in the moments before they perform them. This technique can enhance confidence in the performer and turn their focus from their feelings of anxiety to the feelings of performing the skill. To be successful at this skill, the mental rehearsal needs to engage all the senses and be practised regularly. Practice needs to be adapted to suit the demands of the task. For example, a high jumper knows exactly the situation that they are going into so they can practise an exact skill. It is more difficult for a performer in an open sport, such as football or rugby, but they can practise a range of scenarios they may find themselves in and also specific match situations. They may rehearse what they will do if they find themselves ahead or behind in a match.

The effectiveness of imagery relies on an individual having well-developed imagery skills and they may need to practise developing pictures in their mind. Imagery is effective because it helps to develop the neural pathways between the brain and the muscles; the stronger this pathway becomes, the greater the likelihood that a positive response will be produced by a performer. A person who is mentally rehearsing a skill is often seen to be twitching the muscles involved as a nervous impulse is sent to the muscles. This impulse is not strong enough to produce a full muscle contraction but it is still strengthening the pathway between the brain and the muscles.

Key point: Imagery

Imagery is the recreation of images in your mind. It can be used for relaxation or to mentally rehearse a sports skill or performance.

▶ Systematic desensitization

This is a cognitive relaxation technique developed by Wolpe (1958). It involves placing an anxious individual in increasingly anxiety-making situations and getting them used to each stage before moving on to the next. It is often used to help people deal with phobias or irrational fears. For example, for someone who has a phobia of spiders (a very common phobia) the stages could look like this:

1 The person sits in a room next to a room with a spider in it.

2 The person sits in the room with the spider but the spider is enclosed in a cage.

3 The person is in the room with a dead spider close to them.

4 The person is in a room with a live spider close to them.

5 The person handles the dead spider.

6 The person handles the live spider.

Each stage is more anxiety-making than the previous one, and once their anxiety response to each situation is reduced they move to the next stage. It is often complemented by the use of relaxation techniques in each situation. This technique is used effectively to deal with phobias of flying and of snakes. But how does it relate to sport?

In sport an athlete may be exposed to increasingly anxiety-making situations as they rise from playing for their school to playing for county teams and then playing nationally and internationally. The environments they play in change, the number of people watching increases and the quality of the competition improves. If an athlete is thrown into these environments without preparation, the effect can be disastrous as they don't have the experience to deal with them. To take an extreme example, a non-league football team going to play at a Premiership club is unlikely ever to have heard the noise a 50,000-strong crowd makes. A coach could use a desensitization strategy such as introducing crowd noise when they train or taking the team to the ground to allow the players to become familiar with the environment prior to the match.

There are many other techniques to control arousal and anxiety levels, such as breathing control, autogenic training, biofeedback and even hypnosis.

Summary

This chapter has introduced you to important topics in sports psychology. The studies of motivation, arousal and anxiety are central to any understanding of sports psychology. Also highlighted here are areas of more recent research into topics such as fixed and growth mindsets, passion and perfectionism that are growing in importance. While it is important to have a detailed knowledge of theory, it is also important to take time to reflect on theory and really consider how it can be applied to sport. Sports psychology has huge implications for people involved in sport at all levels of performance, whether as performers, coaches, teachers, parents or even spectators.

Dig deeper

Online resources

Association for Applied Sport Psychology
www.appliedsportpsych.org

Exercise and Sport Psychology
www.vanguard.edu/psychology/amoebaweb/exercise-psychology

Mind Tools
www.mindtools.com/page11.html

The Sport in Mind
www.thesportinmind.com

Sport Psychology Portal (University of Essex)
http://orb.essex.ac.uk/bs/sportpsy

Books

R.H. Cox, *Sport Psychology: Concepts and Applications*, 7th edn (Missouri: McGraw-Hill, 2012).

D. Lavalee, J. Kremer, A.P. Moran and M. Williams, *Sport Psychology: Contemporary Themes* (Basingstoke: Palgrave MacMillan, 2012).

D. Tod, J. Thatcher and R. Rahman, *Sport Psychology* (Basingstoke: Palgrave MacMillan, 2010).

R.S. Weinberg and D. Gould, *Foundations of Sport and Exercise Psychology*, 5th edn (Champaign, IL: Human Kinetics, 2015).

J.M. Williams and V. Krane, *Applied Sport Psychology: Personal Growth to Peak Performance*, 7th edn (Boston: McGraw-Hill, 2015).

1 Which of the following statements illustrates a growth mindset?
   a People with more natural talent than me will always beat me
   b It is more important to keep working hard than rely on natural talent
   c Some things I will never be good at
   d Intelligence is something that comes naturally to some people

2 Low achievers tend to choose which types of opponents?
   a Opponents much worse than them
   b Opponents where they have a 50:50 chance of winning
   c Opponents slightly better than them
   d Opponents slightly worse than them

3 Which of the following is *not* a motivation factor for intrinsically motivated individuals?
   a Gaining knowledge
   b Gaining rewards
   c Gaining feelings of accomplishment
   d Gaining stimulation

4 Which of the following is a psychological symptom of high arousal?
   a Increased sweating
   b Constantly fidgeting
   c Butterflies in the stomach
   d Inability to concentrate

5 The drive theory of arousal proposes which of the following views of the relationship between arousal and performance?
   a Increases in arousal produce improvements in performance
   b Increases in arousal produce improvements in performance but only to a certain point
   c Increases in arousal cause performance level to rapidly decline
   d Increases in arousal produce improvements in performance for skilled activities

6 Which of the following is *not* a factor that influences performance level according to multidimensional anxiety theory?
   a Cognitive state anxiety
   b Levels of self-confidence
   c Individual interpretation of anxiety
   d Somatic state anxiety

7 The catastrophe theory helps to explain which psychological phenomenon?
   a The zone
   b Under-arousal
   c Choking
   d Flow

8 Which of the following is a characteristic of a dysfunctional perfectionist?
   a High levels of self-confidence
   b Low levels of state anxiety
   c High persistence at a task
   d Motivated by a fear of failure

9 Progressive muscular relaxation is most effective for an individual experiencing what?
- **a** High cognitive anxiety
- **b** Low levels of self-confidence
- **c** High somatic anxiety
- **d** Low levels of arousal

10 Which of the following is *not* a feature of imagery?
- **a** Placing an individual in increasingly stressful situations
- **b** Development of neural pathways from brain to muscles
- **c** Development of images in the mind
- **d** Mentally rehearsal of skills

The basics of biomechanics

Biomechanics is concerned with the forces that act on the human body and the effects that these forces produce (Hay, 1993). In this chapter we will look at how forces impact on sports performance. Forces in sport can be divided into two categories:

▶ forces that are produced internally, within the body, through muscular contractions. These forces are used to propel the whole body either on its own, when running or swimming, or when it is in contact with a ball, such as when playing football or rugby. Internally produced forces are also used to throw objects, transfer force to an object using a racket, club, bat or cue, or produce force against a weight, such as when lifting weights.

▶ forces that act on the body as it moves or attempts to stay in position. These forces would include air (or wind), gravity, water and forces applied by other human bodies in contact sports, such as rugby or American football.

Biomechanics is often seen as a challenging or difficult subject because it involves the application of physics to biological subjects and usually involves a degree of mathematics as well. However, it is a key subject in sports science as it impacts on every sport and its knowledge contributes to improving the performance of every sportsperson. Whether learning, teaching or coaching a sport, principles of biomechanics will be implemented in every single training session. Biomechanics helps us to understand and develop techniques to improve the following:

▶ development of the most effective skills and techniques

▶ analysis and prevention of sports injuries

▶ design of equipment, clothing and footwear.

Sports biomechanists are a feature of many sports science support teams, who work with athletes to analyse and enhance how they move and to improve the efficiency of their movements. They use video and analytical tools with specific computer programmes, such as Dartfish, that can be used to break down movement patterns into tiny, individual segments. They may help us to understand sporting questions, such as why is Usain Bolt so fast, how does Cristiano Ronaldo make a football move around in flight and how can Rory McIllroy hit a golf ball so far?

This chapter looks at two branches of biomechanics: kinematics and kinetics. Kinematics describes the motion of the human body and objects used by sportspeople that are thrown, kicked or transported. It is concerned with subjects such as how quickly does a body move, is the movement consistent and how far has it moved? Kinetics looks at what causes a body to move in the way that it does, i.e. the forces that are impacting on the human body or a projectile.

Linear kinematics

SPEED AND VELOCITY

Before examining speed and velocity we need to be able to differentiate between two other similar terms: distance and displacement.

▶ **Distance** is how far a body or object has moved. For example, if a 400 metre runner runs one lap of an athletics track, the distance they cover is 400 metres.

▶ **Displacement** is how far a body or object has moved in relation to its starting position. The 400 metre runner experiences a displacement of 0 metres as they finished at more or less the same point that they started (assuming they are running in lane 1).

> **Key point:** Distance and displacement
> Distance is a description of how far a body or object has moved, while displacement considers the distance a body or object has moved in relation to its starting position.

Distance and displacement are important when differentiating between speed and velocity. **Speed** is a measure of how quickly a body or object has moved over the distance between their start position and their finish position. It is calculated by dividing the distance covered by the time taken:

$$\text{speed} = \frac{\text{distance covered in metres}}{\text{time taken in seconds}}$$

Speed is measured in metres per second (m/s); if the 400 metre runner covered the distance in 52 seconds, their speed would have been 7.69 m/s.

Velocity is a measure of the displacement that a body or object has experienced. If the 400 metre runner were running around an athletics track, they would have experienced a displacement of 0 metres. Velocity is calculated by dividing the displacement by the time taken to produce this displacement.

$$\text{velocity} = \frac{\text{displacement in metres}}{\text{time taken in seconds}}$$

Velocity is also measured in metres per second; if the 400 metre runner covered the distance in 52 seconds, they would have a velocity of 0 m/s. In fact, it doesn't matter how quickly they covered the 400 metres, they would always have a velocity of 0 as their displacement is always 0. However, if they had run 400 metres in a straight line, their displacement would have been 400 metres and they would have had a velocity of 7.69 m/s.

Knowing the difference between speed and velocity might not have seemed very useful so far; however, most projectiles move at different speeds and velocities because they do not travel in straight lines. For example, a javelin covers a distance in the air that is longer than the distance it has been measured at. The javelin throw may be measured at 60 metres, which is actually its displacement, while it may have travelled a distance of 90 metres as it has been projected high into the air. The displacement of the javelin is dependent on two things: its speed (or velocity) on release and the angle it has been released at.

These two variables are also important for a golfer when planning a shot. Accuracy is important for golfers as well as length. The golf ball behaves differently from a javelin because it will also roll, or run, once it has landed. Its displacement depends upon its speed or velocity as it struck. However, its angle of release is even more important; if it leaves the club at a low angle it will run further than if the angle of release is higher. Thus golf clubs are designed to maximize velocity but also offer golfers the opportunity to hit balls at different angles of release.

Key point: Speed and velocity

Speed is a measure of how quickly a body or object has moved the distance between its start position and its finish position.

Velocity considers the displacement that a body or object has experienced and the time this displacement has taken.

It is probably the case that runners, cyclists, swimmers and rowers are most interested in the speed at which they are moving. However, they may also be interested in another measure of speed, pace. **Pace** is defined as how quickly a set distance is being covered. Pace is almost the opposite to speed because to measure pace, you divide the time taken by the distance covered:

$$\text{pace} = \frac{\text{time taken}}{\text{distance covered}}$$

For example, a half-marathon runner may cover 13 miles in about an hour and a half (91 minutes), giving them a pace of 7 minutes per mile. This could also be expressed as 420 seconds per mile.

ACCELERATION

Acceleration relates to changes in velocity over a specific interval of time. To calculate acceleration, you need to know the velocity of a body or object at the start of an interval of time (v1) and its velocity at the end of an interval of time (v2). The difference between the two velocities is divided by the length of time interval to calculate acceleration. This is represented by the following formula:

$$\text{acceleration} = \frac{\text{change in velocity (v2 - v1)}}{\text{change in time}}$$

For example, if a 100 metre runner ran the race in 11 seconds, their velocity would be calculated as 9.1 m/s. Their initial velocity would been 0 m/s as they were stationary in their blocks. Acceleration would be calculated as:

$$\text{acceleration} = \frac{9.1 - 0}{11}$$

$$\text{acceleration} = 0.818 \text{ m/s}^2$$

However, this figure is not very useful as we know that a sprinter does not accelerate in a uniform way throughout a 100 metre race. Rather, they accelerate in the early to middle stages, hold their pace for as long as they can and then, owing to fatigue, they decelerate towards the end of a race. Likewise, a ball that is struck has its peak velocity immediately after the moment of impact and then decelerates more or less constantly until it is at rest or struck again.

Key point: Acceleration

Acceleration is the measure of how quickly velocity has changed over a specific interval of time.

To understand acceleration further, look at Table 6.1, which presents the split times for each 10 metre section of Usain Bolt's record-breaking 100 metre run in Berlin in 2009, average velocities for each 10 metre section and average acceleration rates over each 10 metre section.

Table 6.1 Split times, velocity and acceleration for each 10 metre section of Usain Bolt's record-breaking 100 metre run (Lee, 2009)

Section	Split time	Velocity	Acceleration
0–10 m	1.89 s	5.29 m/s	2.79 m/s^2
11–20 m	0.99 s	10.1 m/s	**4.8 m/s^2**
21–30 m	0.90 s	11.1 m/s	1.11 m/s^2
31–40 m	0.86 s	11.6 m/s	0.58 m/s^2
41–50 m	0.83 s	12.0 m/s	0.48 m/s^2
51–60 m	0.82 s	12.2 m/s	0.24 m/s^2
61–70 m	**0.81 s**	**12.3 m/s**	0.12 m/s^2
71–80 m	0.82 s	12.2 m/s	−0.12 m/s^2
81–90 m	0.83 s	12.0m/s	−0.24 m/s^2
91–100 m	0.83 s	12.0m/s	0 m/s^2

The table shows that it took Bolt until the 61–70 metre section of the race to reach peak velocity; however, his peak acceleration was achieved very early on, between 11–20 metres, as he comes out of the start phase and picks up speed. He experienced deceleration towards the end of the race but it was fairly minimal and considerably less than the other competitors. When acceleration is recorded as zero, it means that velocity has remained constant.

ACCELERATION DUE TO GRAVITY

Gravity is the invisible force that constantly pushes down on us to keep us attached to the ground. We can overcome gravity temporarily by propelling ourselves upwards through forces that we produce or forces imparted on us by equipment such as a trampoline or bungee rope. However, due to gravity's pull we always return to earth. Many sports involve attempts to overcome the force of gravity for as long possible, e.g. ski jumping and somersaults in gymnastics, and others rely on gravity to take us quickly from a high point to a lower point, e.g. diving and downhill skiing. Because gravity is constant, a falling object or body increases its velocity during its descent. A diver needs to perform their twists and turns early in their descent because their increasing velocity reduces the time they have for the second half of the dive.

Gravity is a constant force that accelerates any falling object or body by 9.81 m/s^2. Acceleration through gravity is actually expressed as −9.81 m/s^2 because its acceleration is downwards and that is regarded as negative, acceleration upwards being positive.

Spotlight: Will a golf ball and a shuttlecock hit the ground at the same time if dropped together?

The answer to this is yes and no! We learn that all objects or bodies accelerate at 9.81m/s² so the golf ball and the shuttlecock should hit the ground at the time. However, they don't because the shape of the shuttlecock and its feathers create greater air resistance. Air resistance acts to decelerate the shuttlecock and thus the golf ball reaches the ground first.

However, if the two objects were dropped together in a vacuum, they would hit the ground at exactly the same time (if dropped from exactly the same height). This would apply to any two objects dropped simultaneously in a vacuum because there is no air resistance present.

Linear kinetics

So far we have examined the movement of objects and bodies and mentioned one force that acts to accelerate or decelerate a body or object – gravity. Linear kinetics focuses on forces, including gravity, that produce or change the motion of a body or object. These forces include air resistance, water and frictional forces.

To understand forces fully we need a working knowledge of Newton's three laws of motion. Sir Isaac Newton (1642–1727) was a physicist and mathematician who discovered many of the relationships that laid the foundations of modern mechanics.

NEWTON'S LAWS OF MOTION

▶ **Law of inertia**

Newton's first law of motion is the law of inertia, which states: *A body will maintain a state of rest or constant velocity unless acted on by an external force that changes its state.*

In other words, a body that is at rest will stay at rest until a force is applied to attempt to move it. If it is a heavy object, such as a large dumb-bell, this force would have to be quite significant. However, once a body is in motion it is similarly resistant to changing its state of motion. Anyone who has ever been hit by a hockey ball or cricket ball will agree that this is the case! This phenomenon that a body is unwilling to change its state of motion is known as inertia. For inertia to be overcome, a force must be applied; so a body at rest overcomes inertia when another body exerts a force on it. Likewise, a body in motion can be slowed down, accelerated or diverted when a second body exerts a force on it. Eventually a body in motion will return to a state of immobility owing to the cumulative effect of all the forces acting on it.

Some sports, such as curling or bowling, are based on the skill of imparting on an object an equal amount of force to the forces that will act on the object over a specific distance. In curling there is minimal friction between the stone and the ice so the stone is released relatively slowly to get it close to the house. In contrast, a crown green bowl is released with relatively high velocity onto a grass surface that will produce greater friction on the ball.

▶ **Law of acceleration**

Newton's second law of motion examines the interrelationships between force, mass and acceleration. The size, or magnitude, of a force is measured in Newtons (N) while the mass of an object is defined as being the quantity of matter in a body, measured in kilograms (kg). For a body with a constant mass, this law states: *A force applied to a body causes an acceleration of that body of a magnitude proportional to the force, in the direction of the force, and inversely proportional to the body's mass.*

In simple terms, if a ball is struck with a bat or racket it will travel in the direction that the force has been applied. If a cricket ball is hit straight back towards the bowler, that is the direction it will travel. It will also travel at a higher speed if more force is applied to it. The acceleration of the body, in this case a cricket ball, is inversely proportional to its mass. This means that if the ball was twice as heavy, it would be accelerated at half the speed.

The relationship between force, mass and acceleration can be expressed as:

$$\text{force} = \text{mass} \times \text{acceleration} \ (F = ma)$$

If a ball has a mass of 2 kg and is struck by a force of 20 N, its acceleration will be 10 m/s^2. However, if the ball had a mass of 4 kg, when it was struck by the force of 20 N its acceleration would only be 5 m/s^2.

▶ **Law of reaction**

Newton's third law of motion states that for every action there will be an equal and opposite reaction. When related to force, the law states: *When one body exerts a force on a second body, the second body exerts a reaction force that is equal in magnitude and opposite in direction on the first body.*

Anyone who has kicked an object, such as a stone or rock, will know that this rule is true! Because the stone can't be moved the reaction force, that is equal and in the opposite direction to the direction it is applied, is painfully felt by your foot. In sporting terms this can be understood by considering a snooker player. When they take a shot the cue imparts a force on the cue ball that propels it across the table; however, the cue ball also imparts a force on the cue that is equal and opposite in direction to the force the cue has imparted on it. The cue has to be held securely to absorb this force. In turn the cue ball will make contact with a second ball and exert a force on it, causing it to start rolling; this second ball will impart an equal and opposite force on the cue ball causing it to decelerate rapidly and often, depending on the angle the ball has been struck, come to a halt.

This law has huge importance in sport, where forces are being continually applied. Every step a runner takes will result in forces, called ground reaction forces, being sent back up the legs and spine. Owing to the resilience and flexibility of bones these forces can be absorbed; however, if the forces become too great or too constant, injury and pain can develop. Running shoes have been designed to reduce the impact of ground reaction forces and allow a runner to train longer and remain injury-free. Ground reaction forces are also influenced by the type of terrain that a runner moves across, the speed that they run at, their mass and which part of their foot strikes the ground.

Key point: Newton's three laws of motion
1   A body at rest or moving with a consistent velocity will remain in that state unless an external force is applied to it.
2   The acceleration of a body is proportional to the force that caused it and will take place in the direction that the force is applied. It is inversely proportional to the mass of the body or object to which it has been applied.
3   For every force that is applied there will be an equal and opposite reaction force.

Having established Newton's laws of motion and their relationship to sports activities, we will now look at forces in more depth.

REACTION FORCES

When we are standing, we apply a force on the ground because of our mass and gravity acting on the mass that is the ground. The forces that are exerted on the ground by an athlete are shown in Figure 6.1.

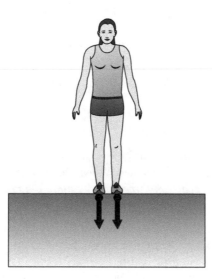

Figure 6.1 The forces an athlete exerts on the ground

This force produces a reaction force upwards into the body equal to the force that is exerted downwards. If the athlete has distributed their weight equally on each foot, there will be equal forces exerted by the ground, as shown in Figure 6.2.

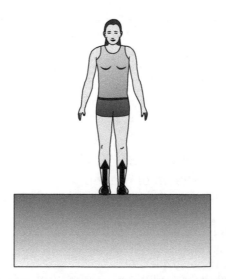

Figure 6.2 The ground exerts forces on the athlete equal and opposite to the forces they exert downwards

When this athlete starts to run, the magnitude and direction of the reaction force changes. The athlete in Figure 6.3 pushes off with one foot at an angle of roughly 45 degrees, and because the direction in which the force has been applied changes, so does the direction of the reaction force. The reaction force will be equal and in the opposite direction to the force applied by the foot. The magnitude of the force will also be increased as the mass of the athlete is no longer being shared between two feet but is now supported by one foot.

Figure 6.3 Changes to ground reaction forces as an athlete starts running

Reaction forces happen in all sports and examples of other reaction forces can be seen in Figure 6.4, where reaction forces applied by a ball, shot put and swimmer's blocks are shown.

Figure 6.4 Three examples of action and reaction forces

AIR RESISTANCE

Air resistance describes the phenomenon that affects the movement of any object as it moves through the atmosphere. Although we can't see them, air is made up of atoms and molecules that strike an object as it passes through them. The object has to move the atoms and molecules aside to enable it to move forwards. Thus air provides a force acting in the opposite direction to an object's direction of travel.

Air resistance, also referred to as drag, is of particular interest to designers of sportswear and sports equipment. The equipment and clothing of cyclists and runners have undergone huge changes over the last 20 years as the effects of air resistance have become better understood.

The helmet and clothing of the cyclist have been specially designed to reduce the force produced by air, as shown in Figure 6.5. The recommended seating position on the bike is also intended to reduce the contact area between the cyclist and air. The outcome of this technique, called streamlining, is that the cyclist is able to travel through air more quickly and to do so with reduced energy expenditure.

Figure 6.5 A cyclist displaying specially designed equipment

Air resistance acts on the human body and also on sporting objects. Figure 6.6 shows the trajectories of a selection of projectiles from different sports.

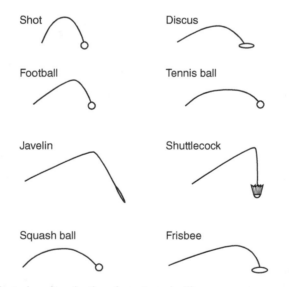

Figure 6.6 Expected trajectories of a selection of sports projectiles

The length of time that a projectile will remain in the air is dependent on several factors.

▶ the angle of trajectory; there is an optimum angle at which to release every projectile. If a javelin is released at too high an angle, it will go up into the air quickly and then come down quickly without travelling very far forwards. If the javelin is released at too low an angle, it will not spend enough time in the air to travel very far.

▶ the speed at which it is released; the greater the speed on release, the further the projectile will travel. For example, the length of time a high jumper or long jumper can remain airborne is dependent on their speed at take-off.

▶ the height from which a projectile is released. It is no coincidence that the winner of the women's discus at the 2012 Olympic Games, Sandra Perkovic of Croatia, is 6 feet tall and the men's champion, Robert Harting of Germany, is 6 feet 7 inches tall. Their height means the point of release is higher than for a shorter athlete.

The flight of the shuttlecock in badminton presents another variable – the shape or design of the projectile. The shuttlecock has the highest release speed of all these projectiles. Feather shuttlecocks can leave the strings of the racket at around 200 mph, and because faster travelling objects come under increased air resistance it also decelerates more quickly. This effect, in combination with the design of the shuttlecock, causes it to decelerate quickly and rapidly drop from its flight path. The feathers of the shuttlecock provide high levels of air resistance and the feathers spread out slightly as the shuttlecock decelerates.

▶ Aerodynamics

Although it is related to air resistance, aerodynamics specifically studies how air flows around an object. The shape of an object influences how air flows around it and this has an impact on sports performance. For example, aerodynamics has major implications for sports such as motor racing and cycling. In motor racing, a car's fuel consumption is affected by air flow around it and a more aerodynamic car will have greater fuel efficiency. This can influence the fuel strategy of the racing team. Similarly, in cycling increased air resistance causes the cyclist to use their fuel stores more quickly. When cycling in the peloton, riders take it in turns to be the lead rider as they experience greater air resistance in this position and thus expend more energy than the riders behind them.

Key point: Air resistance and aerodynamics

Air resistance is the resistance that a body or object will come under when it moves through air. It is caused by the atoms and molecules in air connecting with the body's surface.

Aerodynamics is the study of how air flows around a body or object and the disruption it can cause.

Air flow around an object depends upon the speed of its movement, the shape of the object and the nature of its surface. Figures 6.7 and 6.8 show the effect of speed on the flow of air around a ball. When a ball is moving quickly the layer of air in contact with the ball, called the boundary layer, is slowed down as the ball is exerting a force on it. This layer of air slows down the layer next to it, and so on. As the object passes through air, the layers of air further down the boundary layer become thicker and this causes the air on the boundary layer to become unstable and it starts to get mixed up. The air goes from flowing in parallel lines (laminar flow) to flowing in a violent, mixed-up way (turbulent flow). This turbulent flow creates drag or, more specifically, surface drag. Drag is usually a resistant force and thus acts to slow down the object as it moves around and behind an object.

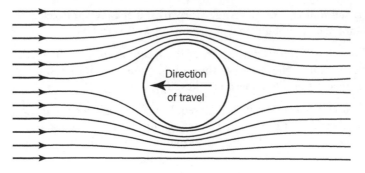

Figure 6.7 Laminar flow of air around a slow-moving ball

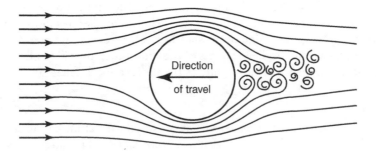

Figure 6.8 Turbulent flow of air around a fast-moving ball, resulting in a drag force

Figure 6.9 demonstrates how the shape of an object affects air flow, showing two different shapes and how air flows around them. The first object is a brick-shaped object and causes turbulence because of its shape but the second object is streamlined and it creates minimal disruption to the air at its boundary layer. This latter shape mirrors the shape of modern cycling helmets, which are specifically designed to reduce drag.

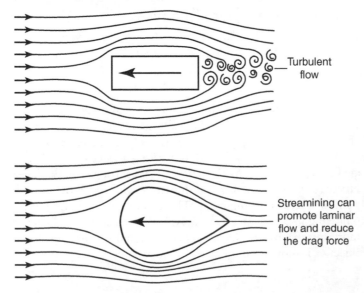

Figure 6.9 Air flow is affected by the shape of the object it moves around

The nature of the surface of the object also affects air flow. If the surface of the object is smooth and shiny, the flow around the object will be predominantly laminar flow (at slow speeds). However, if the surface is rough, the air at the boundary layer will start to be mixed up and turbulent flow will quickly be created, slowing down the object.

Spotlight: Why do cricket balls move in the air?

The science of swing is complex but it is related to two design features of the cricket ball. When it is manufactured a polish is applied to the surface of the ball so that it has a shiny appearance. These shiny surfaces promote laminar flow and a reduced air resistance. The second feature is a sewn seam that stands up above the shiny surfaces; seams on some balls are more pronounced than on other balls. The seam creates disruption with the air molecules at the boundary layer and produces turbulent flow. So in some areas of the ball there is turbulent flow and in others there is laminar flow, and this causes balls to have different flight paths if released at different angles.

A fast bowler will favour a new ball because while it still has its shiny surfaces it can be bowled at its highest speeds due to the predominance of laminar flow around it. However, a swing bowler will ensure that one side of the ball stays highly polished and the other side is dull or roughened up. This will cause the shiny side, which has less turbulent flow, to travel faster through the air than the dull side, which is experiencing more turbulent flow at its boundary layer. Hence the ball will start to move in the air.

Balls tend to move only in certain weather conditions. Overcast, cloudy conditions associated with low pressure are highly conducive to swing bowling, while high pressure conditions with sun and cloudless skies are less conducive to swing bowling. This is to do with the distance between the atoms and molecules in the air. In low pressure conditions, the atoms and molecules are closer together than in high pressure conditions and thus there is greater air resistance. The increased air resistance ensures that there is greater turbulent flow at the boundary layer and thus more potential swing.

In sports where speed is important it is vital to reduce drag by minimizing turbulent flow. This is the reason that swimmers and cyclists choose shiny Lycra clothing and shave their legs before competing, and why the hulls of boats and racing cars appear to be highly polished. It is all to gain those vital few seconds or milliseconds over opponents. Exploiting aerodynamics and minimizing drag is also the reason that cyclists in the peloton ride so close together.

The proximity of cyclists to each other, as shown in Figure 6.10, ensures that air flows around them as if they were a single object rather than three separate objects.

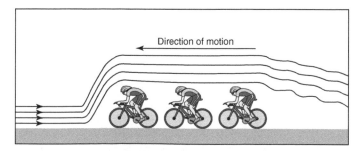

Figure 6.10 Air flow around three cyclists in close proximity to each other

The cyclists must be positioned close together because the leading cyclist disrupts the flow of air molecules at the boundary layer and creates turbulence behind him or herself. This occurs unless the second cyclist is so close that the air also flows directly over them and not behind the first cyclist. This effect will occur down the length of the chain of cyclists, or the peloton, as long as they each ride with their front wheel as close as possible to the back wheel of the rider in front. The impact of increasing the distance between each cyclist is illustrated in Figure 6.11.

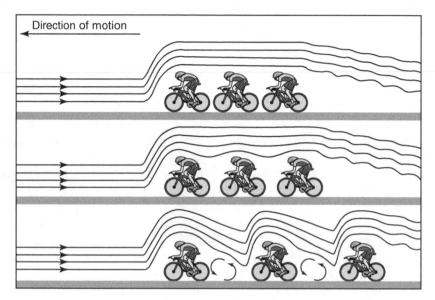

Figure 6.11 Air flow over three cyclists at different distances apart from each other

Unfortunately, an unintended consequence of this close grouping is that if a lead rider crashes, it often results in a spectacular mass crash, the proximity and speed of the riders making it virtually impossible to stop or avoid the fallen cyclist.

Spotlight: If smooth surfaces are more aerodynamic, why do golf balls have dimples?

It does seem counterintuitive that golf balls have dimples, and golf balls did used to be smooth. However, Scottish caddies reputedly discovered that golf balls that were cut or scuffed seemed to stay in the air longer. This led to golf balls being redesigned.

While smooth surfaces tend to be more aerodynamic, the shape of an object is vitally important as well. A smooth golf ball will initially produce laminar flow around it but because of its shape it also causes separation between the layers of air flowing around it. When air strikes the ball, the layers of air close to the ball are pushed closer together but as the layers pass over the ball, they separate again and this separation causes high levels of turbulence, or drag. This is called form drag and causes the ball to rapidly decelerate.

Separation is reduced if there is a small amount of turbulence at the boundary between the golf ball and the first layer of air. Small dimples produce this turbulence and reduce drag by up to 50 per cent. Thus the ball stays in the air longer. However, the depth of the dimples is important and early research showed that a dimple depth of 0.25 mm results in the optimal length of carry.

► Lift

While minimizing drag is important, maximizing a second air resistance force, lift, is also vital for some sports performers. Lift works on a similar principle to drag but at a 90 degree angle to drag. While drag pulls you back, lift pushes you up. A ski jumper aims to take off and travel through the air at a specific angle to increase lift forces, and a discus thrower releases the discus at a specific angle to achieve the same effect. The main factor that influences lift is the shape of the object. The closer the object resembles the shape of a foil (flat on the lower surface and curved on the upper surface), the greater the likelihood of lift occurring. A foil, and the air flow around it, can be seen in Figure 6.12. A foil produces a pressure differential between the air flowing under the foil and the air flowing over the foil. The air under the foil flows slowly, causing a relatively high pressure, while the air on the upper surface flows more quickly because the layers of air are pushed closer together, causing a relatively lower pressure. This pressure differential creates lift forces.

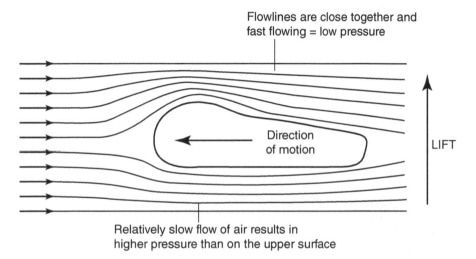

Figure 6.12 Different speeds of air flow around a foil cause a pressure differential between its lower and upper surfaces with a resulting lift effect

This lift principle is illustrated by how the wings of planes are designed; when the wing is at a certain angle, lift is produced and the plane takes off. The principle of lift is also employed by the ski jumper, who overcomes the force of gravity for as long as they can by ensuring that air flows more slowly below them than above them. Unfortunately, gravity always wins and will overcome lift to return them to the ground. The design of Formula 1 racing cars also applies the principle of lift, in this case using an aerofoil that is inverted so that the air travels more quickly on the lower surface than the upper surface and a downward force is produced, resulting in improved road-holding and cornering capabilities. This relationship between speed of air flow and air pressure is known as the Bernoulli principle or effect.

Key point: The Bernoulli effect

The Bernoulli effect explains lift and is based on the principle that different air velocities produce differentials in pressure. If air flows at a higher velocity over the upper surface of an object than its lower surface, it will have a relatively lower pressure and the result will be lift.

▶ **The Magnus effect**

The Magnus effect applies the principles of the Bernoulli effect of pressure differentials to spinning objects. When an object spins, the air molecules forming the boundary edge spin with it. The air molecules at the boundary edge come under resistance from the air flow that it is travelling into. This is shown in Figure 6.13, where a ball is moving forwards into an air flow but is also spinning in a clockwise direction. The collision between these two sets of moving air molecules causes changes in pressure. As the ball is spinning clockwise, the air molecules on the left-hand side of the ball are colliding head-on with the air flow and creating high pressure and a lower velocity. The air molecules on the right-hand side are flowing in the same direction as the air flowing over them so the collision between the two is minimal, creating a higher velocity and lower pressure than on the left side. As a result the ball will move, or spin, to the right. This movement has been caused by the creation of a Magnus force.

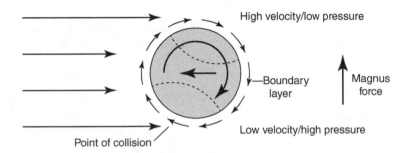

Figure 6.13 The collision between air molecules at the boundary layer and in the air flow creates a Magnus force

This Magnus effect has application to all sports involving a ball. Some balls are more susceptible to spin than others. For example, tennis balls are covered in felt, which acts to trap a large area of boundary air to collide with the air flow and thus creates a heightened Magnus effect. It also explains how free kicks in soccer can be made to swerve if the ball is struck in a specific way to cause it to rotate.

🔑 **Key point:** The Magnus effect

The Magnus effect explains why balls deviate from a straight path when they are rotating, or spin. Spin is caused by the air molecules at the boundary layer moving in different directions in relation to the air flow.

WATER RESISTANCE

▶ **Three phases of matter**

Before looking at the forces offered by water, it is worth looking at the properties of gas, liquids and solids so that you can appreciate why movement through each type of matter is so different. Water is a good example of a substance that can be found in different phases. As well as its liquid form, water can be found in its solid form (ice) and its gas form (steam), depending on its temperature.

But what is the difference between the three forms? The form water takes is dependent on how closely packed the atoms and molecules are and the strength of the bonds between them. Figure 6.14 shows the proximity of molecules in each of the three phases.

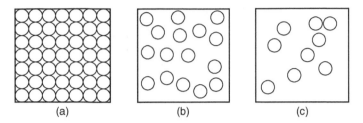

Figure 6.14 Internal structures of (a) solids, (b) liquids and (c) gases

Solids have atoms or molecules packed closely together with strong bonds between them. There is little space between the molecules, making it very difficult for another object to pass through them. In liquids, the atoms and molecules are still quite closely packed but there are weak bonds between them. There is enough space for another object to move between the atoms and molecules. The viscosity or thickness of a liquid is influenced by the proximity of the atoms and molecules within the liquid and the strength of the bonds between them. In a gas, however, the atoms and molecules have large distances between them and no bonds. The atoms and molecules can move freely around the space that they occupy.

▶ Buoyancy

When an object sits in water it experiences a downwards force caused by gravity. The object either sinks or floats; this is dependent on the upward force of buoyancy. Buoyancy is the opposite force to gravity and is exerted on the object by water due to the density of water. If an object is denser than water it will sink, and if it is less dense it will float. The density of any object is dependent on its mass and its size. For example, a snooker ball will sink because its mass is large for its size while a table tennis ball will float because it has a low mass for its size.

The strength of a buoyant force is based on a law called Archimedes' principle, which says that the size of the buoyant force acting on a body is equal to the weight of the water that it displaces. For a swimmer, the buoyant force that acts on their body is equal to the weight of the water that they push out of the way when they are immersed in water. When the size of this force is greater than the force of gravity pushing downwards, the swimmer will float.

There is a relationship between body type and whether a body sinks or floats. A swimmer who is predominantly muscle and bone has a greater density than a swimmer with more body fat and less muscle (muscle is over three times heavier than fat). Because of their greater density, the muscular athlete is less likely to float than the swimmer with more body fat and a lower body density. This is a difficult balance for a competitive swimmer to achieve; they need muscle to produce force to propel themselves through the water but too much muscle reduces buoyancy. Typically, competitive swimmers have wide, muscular shoulders but less muscular legs.

Key point: Buoyancy

Buoyancy is a force that acts upwards in opposition to gravity due to the density of the water or liquid in which an object is placed.

▶ Forces acting on the swimmer

A swimmer, or another object moving through water, has at least four forces acting them, as can be seen in Figure 6.15. These are:

▶ the reaction force (F), caused by the swimmer kicking against the water and producing a force in the same direction as the swimmer's movement

▶ water resistance, or drag (D), caused by the swimmer colliding with the molecules in the water; this force is applied in the opposite direction to the swimmer's movement

▶ buoyancy force (B), which is pushing upwards

▶ weight (W), which is pushing downwards owing to the force of gravity.

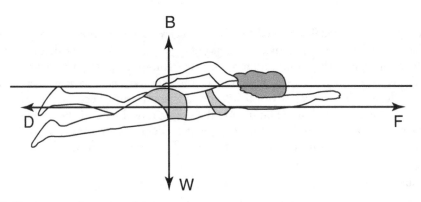

Figure 6.15 The forces acting on a swimmer

The greatest consideration for the swimmer is to minimize drag and they do this by adopting a streamlined position in the water. They should remain flat, close to the surface and avoid dropping their feet and legs. The less of their body they have in contact with water, the less drag they produce; wearing a shiny swimsuit and a swimming hat and removing body hair also minimizes drag. Unfortunately for the swimmer, the faster they swim the more drag they produce, but because the aim is to swim fast this cannot be prevented. They must work on techniques to minimize the drag their body creates.

FRICTION

Friction is defined as a force that opposes the effort to slide or roll one body over another (Hamilton, Weimar and Luttgens, 2008). Friction between our shoes and the ground is central to our ability to walk and run. Lack of friction can be hazardous, such as when we walk on a wet or icy surface. Most sports rely on friction or creating friction between two surfaces; for example, when a gymnast puts chalk on their hands to increase their chances of staying on a piece of apparatus or a hockey player chooses footwear appropriate to a playing surface. Sliding sports, such as snowboarding and skeleton bobsleigh, are concerned with minimizing friction so that velocity can be maximized.

Friction occurs when two surfaces come into contact and exert a force on each other. If you rub the palms of your hands together, you will feel some resistance to the movement. Friction is the resistance force that opposes the movement of the hands. If your hands were wet there would be less friction, and if they were covered in chalk there would be more friction. When two surfaces are in contact, the atoms on each surface form a weak bond, and to allow the surfaces to move these weak bonds must be broken.

Key point: Friction

Friction is a force that arises when two surfaces come into contact with each other and exert a force on each other.

The amount of friction depends upon the nature of surfaces in contact – smooth surfaces create less friction than rough ones – but also on the forces that are pressing them together. The area of the surface is not important; for example, it takes as much force to push a heavy box flat on the ground as it takes to push it if it was balanced on its edge. If you were to push a heavy box gently across a carpet, you would find that it was resistant to movement. This resistance is owing to the friction between the box and the carpet it is standing on. If you push harder, eventually the box will start to slide because the force you have applied is now greater than the frictional force. The pushing force that you apply will be in the opposite direction to the frictional force between the box and the carpet.

Spotlight: Rafael Nadal – the king of clay

Up to the beginning of 2015, Rafael Nadal had won 14 Open tennis championships, including Wimbledon and the US Open twice, the Australian Open once and the French Open nine times. In fact, between 2005 and 2014 he won the French Open nine times out of the 10 tournaments he played.

Why has he been so disproportionately successful at the French Open? The answer is to do with friction.

Tennis tournaments are played on three different surfaces – grass at Wimbledon, hard courts at the Australian and US Open and clay at the French Open. Grass and hard courts have very little friction and offer little resistance to hard tennis balls. As a result these surfaces favour players who have fast, powerful serves and hit the ball hard, such as Novak Djokovic (four Australian Open titles 2011–15) and Roger Federer (seven Wimbledon titles 2003–12).

The courts at Roland Garros in Paris are made of rough clay that provides more friction than other surfaces. This friction acts to decelerate the ball and reduce the effectiveness of powerful serves, and therefore of serve-and-volley type players. Clay gives players like Nadal more time to play their shots. Nadal is able to defend the serve and then counterattack his opponent. His game is based on endurance, long rallies and playing passing shots past these powerful opponents.

Types of friction

Different types of friction occur depending on the situation. There are three main types:

- static friction, which occurs when two objects push against each other but neither one moves, e.g. a runner pushing against the ground

- sliding friction, which occurs when a body moves across a surface, e.g. a skier moving down a slope

- rolling friction, which occurs when a hockey player passes a hockey ball to a teammate.

Each of these involves a difference in the movement between two surfaces. Static friction may become sliding or rolling friction if the size of the force exerted increases. The change from static to sliding friction depends on the size of the force applied. A runner's foot will not slide backwards as long as the force they exert does not overcome the friction forces. If they exert too much force in relation to the friction between the two surfaces, their foot will move backwards. Running shoes, and particularly spiked shoes, are designed to maximize friction relevant to specific surfaces. The amount of friction created between two surfaces is represented by the coefficient of friction.

Coefficient of friction

The coefficient of friction is a unitless number that represents the relative ease of sliding between two surfaces in contact (Hall, 2007). It is influenced by the relative hardness and roughness of the two surfaces and the extent to which the molecules of each surface create bonds. The coefficient of friction between a training shoe's rubber sole and a tartan-surfaced athletics track would be relatively high in comparison to that of a skating blade and ice surface. Table 6.2 shows coefficients of friction for selected surfaces.

Table 6.2 The coefficients of friction for selected surfaces (Serway and Jewett, 2014)

Types of surfaces	Coefficient of friction
Rubber on concrete	1.0
Ice on ice	0.1
Waxed wood on snow	0.14
Copper on steel	0.53

This coefficient is dependent on other substances present at the point where the two surfaces meet. In particular, liquids decrease the coefficient of friction. This may be done deliberately to reduce friction, such as oiling the chain and other moving points of a bicycle. Footballers change their boots depending on the wetness of the surface to increase friction and ensure they stay upright. Liquids reduce friction because they disrupt the electrical forces between the atoms that bond between the two forces by weakening it significantly.

Key point: The coefficient of friction

The coefficient of friction represents the ease or resistance to sliding between two surfaces in contact with each other.

Spotlight: When do racing cars use different types of tyres?

In 2014, Formula 1 racing teams had a choice of six types of tyre to put on their cars. Their choices illustrate two characteristics of friction:

1 Smooth surfaces provide less friction than ridged or grooved surfaces.

2 Soft surfaces create more friction than hard ones.

Teams can choose between treaded tyres and slick tyres (smooth tyres). Slick tyres are used when the track is dry, but there are four different types of slick tyres. At one end of the scale are the super-soft tyres that create the most friction but have limited durability as the rubber is quickly worn away. At the other end are hard tyres that are more durable but produce less friction. Friction is vital when accelerating at the start of the race and when taking corners or chicanes at speed. In dry conditions teams usually choose soft or medium tyres, which provide a balance of friction and durability.

Treaded tyres are used to improve grip on wet tracks because of the greater friction they produce with the track. When the track is wet, the tyre exerts a downwards force that pushes the water on the track between the grooves of the tyre and then away from the tyre. The tread provides channels for the water that slick tyres cannot. This creates a potentially dryer and more secure surface between the tyre and the track and thus better grip in wet conditions. There are two types of treaded tyre: intermediates for when it is raining but there is no standing water, and wet for when there is standing water on the track.

▶ Friction and the human body

Human movement is made possible by the movement of joints where two bones articulate with each other. Synovial joints have been designed to minimize absolutely friction between the two hard ends of the bones. In fact they have a coefficient of friction of around 0.01 (Serway and Jewett, 2014), which is significantly lower than any other two compounds. Two features of synovial joints are, first, the presence of articular cartilage at the ends of bone. Cartilage is a highly elastic substance that is soft but very durable. The second feature is that joints are bathed in synovial fluid, which is a viscous oil-like substance. Synovial fluid lubricates the joint and reduces friction within it. Like oil, as synovial fluid becomes warmer it becomes thinner and works more effectively at keeping the moving parts lubricated. This is one reason why a warm-up is important before exercise, so that the effects of friction are minimized. Joint conditions, such as osteoarthritis, can develop if there is a loss of articular cartilage and the two hard ends of bones start to rub together. Osteoarthritis is characterized by pain and swelling but also redness because of the heat caused by the frictional forces between the two bones.

Friction is also a problem for runners and cyclists. Frictional forces are created when one body part is moving across another or clothing is consistently moving across a body part. This friction causes heat and can result in surface skin being rubbed away. If this is happening for 26 miles during a marathon or during a triathlon of even longer duration, it is going to be very uncomfortable. Most experienced runners and cyclists are aware of this problem and they use lubricants such as Vaseline to reduce friction.

CENTRE OF GRAVITY

The centre of gravity is also referred to as the centre of mass. It is the balance point of an object or body at which there is an equal weight force on both sides (Burkett, 2010). If we were to hold a 12 inch ruler at exactly the point where there is equal weight on each side, it would be perfectly balanced, and that would be the centre of its mass and the point through which the force of gravity is acting. Because a ruler is a uniform shape, it is easy to identify its centre of gravity. However, finding the centre of gravity in the human body is more difficult because it is made up of a central area of mass, the torso, with additional components – the head, arms and legs – attached to it. Added to that, different tissues have different densities; for example, muscle is heavier than fat. The centre of gravity depends on the position of the limbs in relation to the torso, as shown in Figure 6.16. Our centre of gravity is not located at the central point of our body because the top half of our body contains roughly 60 per cent of our mass and the lower body the remaining 40 per cent. The centre of gravity in a human is located roughly below the navel between the front of the hip bones or in front of the second sacral vertebra, as can be seen in the first image in Figure 6.16. It would be approximately midway between the front and back of the body.

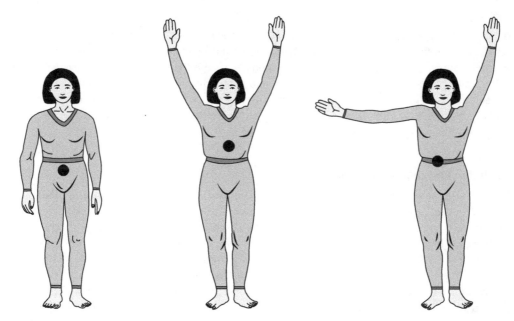

Figure 6.16 The centre of gravity of a human body moves as the body changes position

It should be stressed that the centre of gravity is a theoretical point rather than a real place because it may not always lie within the physical bounds of a person. For example, if you kneel on all fours, your centre of gravity would have moved significantly and would now be in a position slightly in front of your body. Specifically, it would be found just in front of your lower stomach.

Key point: The centre of gravity

The centre of gravity is the point where a body's mass is equally balanced. It is the point through which gravity acts.

The centre of gravity is important when analysing the motion of the human body because if the centre of gravity travels too far forwards, backwards or to one side of the body, balance will be lost. Rugby players and footballers are often praised if they have a low centre of gravity because it means that they don't fall over as easily and can assume greater ranges of motion without losing their balance. In sports where maintaining balance is central to performance, such as gymnastics, we tend to find athletes who are short of stature and thus have a centre of gravity that is relatively close to the ground. For example, Claudia Fragapane, who won four gold medals at the 2014 Commonwealth Games, is 4 feet 6 inches in height. This means that if she were to perform a cartwheel, her centre of gravity would not travel as far forwards or backwards as a much taller gymnast's.

▶ Centre of mass and the high jump

While gymnasts tend to be of short stature so that their centre of gravity stays relatively close to their body, the opposite is true for high jumpers. High jumpers are usually relatively tall with long limbs and this means that their centre of gravity is relatively higher in their body. For example, Blanka Vlasic, who has won two World Championship gold medals, is 6 feet 4 inches, and Javier Sotomayor, the men's world record holder (as at 2014), is 6 feet 5 inches.

Figure 6.17 shows the technique that is currently most popular among high jumpers. It is known as the Fosbury flop, after Dick Fosbury who pioneered the technique and used it to win the gold medal at the 1968 Olympic Games.

Figure 6.17 A high jumper using the Fosbury flop technique

The major determinant of success in the high jump is velocity at take-off, as this influences the height the athlete will gain. However, once the athlete is in the air they can manipulate the location of their centre of gravity so that although their body goes over the bar, their centre of gravity passes below it. The technique involves bending the back as much as possible and keeping the legs hanging until the point when the hips could dislodge the bar, then rapidly raising the hips and pulling the legs over the bar. Because the top athletes have long bodies and limbs, it enables them to move their centre of gravity further away from their body than a shorter person.

▶ Centre of gravity and stability

Stability is a term that is closely related to the concept of balance and is described as resistance to the disruption of equilibrium (Hall, 2007). Stability is vital to a rugby player trying to resist a tackle or a wrestler trying to remain on their feet. Sprinters are at the last point before unbalance when they are in the start position on the blocks; the tiniest of movements can cause them to lose their balance and move forwards. While a lower centre of gravity promotes stability, this is also influenced by another factor: the size of the base of support. The base of support is determined by the size of the bases, which is the feet in humans, and the width that the bases are apart. Clearly, a person standing on one leg has relatively poor stability, while stability increases as the distance between their two feet increases. Martial artists are aware of this and ensure a wide stable base is adopted as a means of providing stability for their defence and a stable base from which to attack their opponent. A split position, with one foot in front of the other while maintaining a wide base, is also relatively stable. This stance is often used by weightlifters.

Centre of gravity and balance are important issues for older people. As a person gets older, they often become stooped owing to the impact of 70 years of gravity pushing downwards on their bodies. Osteoporosis is a disease that is characterized by an osteoporotic stoop, where the spine is significantly bent forwards, owing to the thinning of bones in the spine. The effect of the stoop is to cause the centre of gravity to move forwards and the resulting reduction of balance makes falls more common. Unfortunately, because osteoporosis is characterized by a loss of bone density, fractures, particularly at the hip, are also more likely as a result of a fall.

Key point: Stability

Stability is described as a body's resistance to the disruption of its balance.

Summary

The application of biomechanical principles enables us to understand the movement of the human body and objects in sporting environments. This understanding helps coaches and sports teachers to advise on appropriate techniques to improve the performances of athletes and to minimize the risk of injury.

This chapter looked at two key subjects within the field of biomechanics: linear kinematics, which describes the motion of the human body and sporting objects; and linear kinetics, which describes the forces that act on the human body and sporting objects during performance.

Understanding biomechanical principles can be challenging and may demand more time and effort than other subjects within sports science. However, its study is highly rewarding as it offers a framework for understanding the performance of every single athlete. Sports performance always involves the movement of the human body, or parts of it, and often sporting objects as well. These movements are always governed by the principles of biomechanics.

Dig deeper

Online resources

Australian Sports Commission
www.ausport.gov.au/ais/performance_support/movement_science/biomechanics

British Association of Sport and Exercise Science
www.bases.org.uk/Biomechanics

Gait and Clinical Movement Analysis Society
www.gcmas.org/about

International Society of Biomechanists
http://isbweb.org

Quintic software for analysis of sports
www.quintic.com

Sports Training Advisor
www.sports-training-adviser.com/sportbiomechanics.html

Books

R. Bartlett, *Introduction to Sports Biomechanics*, 2nd edn (Abingdon: Routledge, 2007).

A. Blazevich, *Sports Biomechanics – The Basics: Optimising Human Performance* (London: A & C Black, 2007).

B. Burkett, *Sports Mechanics for Coaches*, 3rd edn (Champaign, IL: Human Kinetics, 2010).

S.J. Hall, *Basic Biomechanics*, 5th edn (New York: McGraw-Hill, 2007).

N. Hamilton, W. Weimar and K. Luttgens, *Kinesiology: Scientific Basis of Human Motion* (Boston: McGraw-Hill, 2008).

C.J. Payton and R.M. Bartlett (eds), *Biomechanical Evaluation and Movement in Sport and Exercise* (Abingdon: Routledge, 2008).

D. Sewell, P. Watkins and M. Griffin, *Sport and Exercise Science* (Abingdon: Hodder Arnold, 2005).

R. Wirhed, *Athletic Ability and the Anatomy of Motion*, 3rd edn (London: Elsevier, 2006).

Fact-check

1 Which of the following is the correct equation for calculating velocity?
  a Distance covered ÷ time taken
  b Displacement ÷ time taken
  c Time taken ÷ distance covered
  d Time taken ÷ displacement

2 If a 100 metre runner ran a race in 12 seconds, what would be their acceleration over the length of the race?
  a 0.80 m/s^2
  b 0.71 m/s^2
  c 0.65 m/s^2
  d 0.69 m/s^2

3 Which of the following is an example of a reaction force?
  a A javelin thrower imparts force on the javelin
  b The force a ball exerts on the person kicking it
  c The force of a cricket bat on the ball it is striking
  d A swimmer pushes into their blocks when they start a race

4 Which of the following will *not* impact on the air flow around an object?
  a Its mass
  b Its speed
  c Its shape
  d Its surface

5 Which of the following is a feature of laminate flow?
  a Produces drag
  b Air flows in parallel lines
  c Air flows in a mixed-up way
  d Production of a resistant force

6 Which is the main factor that influence the strength of lift forces?
  a The speed of the object
  b The surface area of the object
  c The size of the object
  d The shape of the object

7 What does the Magnus effect explain?
  a Why objects stay in the air for different lengths of time
  b Why balls can spin and deviate from a straight path
  c Why some objects decelerate more quickly than others
  d Why some objects produce more drag than others

8 What is the greatest factor that influences whether an object will float or sink?
  a The density of the object
  b The size of the object
  c The effect of gravity
  d The shape of the object

9 Which of the following is *not* a type of friction?
   a   Static friction
   b   Dynamic friction
   c   Sliding friction
   d   Rolling friction

10 Why is a low centre of gravity beneficial to a football player?
   a   It means they can move more quickly
   b   It means they can jump more easily
   c   It means they are less likely to fall over
   d   It means they are less likely to be injured

7

Introducing sports nutrition

Sports nutrition is an area of research that has grown significantly over the past 30 years. This is because the nutritional status of an athlete has a huge impact on their performance. How they eat during the training period and to recover from training influences their health and their fitness levels; nutrition is vital after exercise to enable the body to recover from training sessions and before exercise to determine how well the body will allow someone to perform. Athletes are always looking for that extra competitive edge and are interested in the range of supplements available to support their diet and performance. For some athletes it can be physically difficult to get enough calories a day but the timing of when nutrients are introduced into the body is also vitally important.

This chapter introduces the basics of nutrition so that you know what is meant by carbohydrates, protein and fats and then examines what an athlete's diet should look like, when they should be eating, whether they should be taking supplements, etc. Current areas of interest in nutrition and some of the current arguments about nutrition are also examined.

It is important to understand the basics of nutrition so that you can understand and analyse the information that is presented to you. Our society seems to have an obsession with nutrition, partly because everyone eats but probably also because it is related to how we look and our health. Articles about nutrition appear regularly in newspapers and magazines as well as on a multitude of resources online. However, these articles often contradict one another or are written from one author's perspective. If you understand the basic principles of nutrition, you can critically analyse articles and make judgements about what the authors are saying.

Macronutrients and micronutrients

There are two significant differences between macronutrients and micronutrients:

▶ macronutrients – carbohydrates, fats and proteins – are nutrients that are needed in large amounts in our diets; micronutrients – vitamins and minerals – are needed in our diets as well but only in smaller amounts

▶ macronutrients yield energy, or contain calories, while micronutrients do not.

Table 7.1 summarizes the main sources and functions of macro and micronutrients.

Table 7.1 Main sources, functions and contribution to the diet of macronutrients and micronutrients

Nutrient	Sources	Functions	Energy yield	% kcal contribution to diet
Carbohydrates	Bread, rice, pasta, potatoes	Provide energy to the brain and nervous system, liver, heart and muscles	1 g yields 4 kcal	50–60% of kcal
Proteins	Meat, fish, eggs, dairy products	Form structures of the body; production of hormones and enzymes	1 g yields 4 kcal	10–20 % of kcal
Fats	Animal fats, butter, oils	Provide energy; component of structures of the body; production of hormones	1 g yields 9 kcal	30% of kcal
Vitamins	Fruit, vegetables	Energy production; immunity	0	0% of kcal
Minerals	Fruit, vegetables	Structures of the body; energy production	0	0% of kcal

This table is meant to serve as a summary, and the sources and functions of each nutrient are only a selection rather than being exhaustive. Water is often seen as being the 'sixth nutrient' but because it has no calorie content and very little nutritional value it has been left out of this table. That said, you could only survive for two to three days without drinking water so it clearly has a key role to play in any nutritional plan.

As the table shows, there is considerable difference in energy content between carbohydrates, proteins and fats. Equal amounts of carbohydrates and fats or proteins and fats do not yield equal energy as fats contain around just over two times as much energy as carbohydrates and proteins. As a result, foods high in fat are described as being 'energy dense'. This difference has been the cause, probably mistakenly, of fats being given a low priority in nutrition.

Spotlight: What is a calorie?

A calorie is the measurement used to express the energy in food, but it is actually the amount of heat required to raise the temperature of 1 litre (or 1 kilogram) of water by 1°C. Strictly speaking, we should use the term 'kilocalorie', or 'kcal', as a calorie would only raise the temperature of 1 ml of water by 1°C.

Some countries use joules as a measure of energy and the relationship between calories and joules is that 1 kilocalorie = 4.2 kjoules (or kj).

Key point: Macronutrients and micronutrients

Macronutrients are nutrients that are needed in large amounts and contain energy. Micronutrients are needed in smaller amounts and contain no energy.

Carbohydrates, proteins and fats are macronutrients, and vitamins and minerals are micronutrients.

Why is nutrition important?

Nutrition is important because it provides energy for the various processes of the body. Energy is needed for the brain and nervous system to produce and transmit nervous impulses, for the digestive system to break down and transport nutrients, for the repair of damaged tissues that occurs on a daily basis and for movement. The brain uses between 500–600 kcal per day and the liver and digestive system around 300–400 kcal per day. Under normal circumstances, these organs are predominantly dependent on glucose, and thus have a glucose requirement of around 1000 kcal per day between them.

Nutrition is also important because it is closely related to the health of individual cells and the human body as a whole. All cells need a steady supply of energy in the form of carbohydrates and fats, protein to repair any damage, vitamins and minerals to allow chemical reactions to take place at the necessary rate, and water. They also require oxygen for energy production. The quality of the nutrients we supply to our cells directly affects the quality of the structure and function of cells, and ultimately the quality of the structure and function of our body.

Key point: We are what we eat!

What we feed our cells directly affects the quality of their structure and function. Thus nutrition impacts on our health and performance levels.

Carbohydrates

Carbohydrates are found in plentiful supply in foods such as grains, rice, vegetables, fruit, sweets, fizzy drinks, cakes and biscuits. They form the basis of most modern human diets. Carbohydrates are found in different forms but all carbohydrate foods are eventually broken down into glucose. The majority of digestion occurs in the small intestine, where digestive enzymes break down carbohydrate foods into saccharides, such as glucose and fructose, and then they enter the bloodstream. From the bloodstream, glucose is taken to the brain to be used as energy and any excess glucose is stored in the muscles and the liver.

The muscles are able to store around 300 g or 1200 kcal of glucose as glycogen, so it is available for when exercise starts. The liver can store around 100 g or 400 kcal of glucose as glycogen, and it is available to be returned into the bloodstream to be taken to the brain if it becomes short of glucose. Glycogen is the term for stored glucose, and glucose needs to be attached to water to enable its storage in muscles and the liver.

CARBOHYDRATES, SACCHARIDES AND SUGARS

Terminology with regard to nutrition can be tricky as carbohydrates, saccharides, glucose and sugar tend to be used interchangeably but there are differences between them. 'Saccharides' is the term for the different categories of carbohydrates or types of sugars: monosaccharides, disaccharides, oligosaccharides and polysaccharides. However, 'sugar' has multiple meanings as it is used as an umbrella term for monosaccharides and disaccharides, but also as a term for the refined saccharides we add to our food or drinks at the table (table sugar). On food labels, sugar refers to monosaccharides and disaccharides. Sugar is currently the subject of debate in nutrition and is seen as the cause for many nutrition-related health problems, such as obesity and type 2 diabetes. However, sugar has different forms and not all sugars should be treated as 'bad'.

▶ Monosaccharides

A monosaccharide is one unit of a sugar. As shown in Figure 7.1, there are three types:

▶ glucose

▶ fructose

▶ galactose.

Glucose is commonly available in most carbohydrate foods, fructose is found in fruits and galactose is found as a component of milk sugars. In the digestive system, carbohydrate foods are broken down into either glucose, fructose or galactose, and glucose is directly used for energy or stored. However, fructose and galactose cannot be used directly for energy and they are transported to the liver where they are slowly converted into glucose before being reintroduced into the bloodstream. Consequently, fructose and galactose become available as energy at a much slower rate than glucose and this has an important impact, as we shall see when we look at the glycaemic index.

▶ Disaccharides

Disaccharides are two units of sugar joined by a bond. As shown in Figure 7.1, there are three types, which are made up of a combination of monosaccharides:

▶ sucrose (= glucose + fructose)

▶ lactose (= glucose + galactose)

▶ maltose (= glucose + glucose)

Sucrose is found naturally in most carbohydrate foods, including cane sugar, brown sugar, syrups and honey. It is also what we refer to as 'table sugar'. Lactose is found in milk, cheese and yoghurts, and maltose is found in malt breads and some beers.

Key point: Glucose

Glucose is the smallest unit of a carbohydrate. All carbohydrates, irrespective of their source, eventually become glucose.

As a group, mono- and disaccharides are referred to as 'simple sugars' or 'simple carbohydrates'. They are often neglected in athletes' diets as they are seen as lacking nutrient value or described as 'empty calories', meaning that they lack vitamins and minerals. While this is true to a certain extent, their true nutritional value is based on whether they have been refined or remain in their natural state, as seen in Table 7.2. For example, fruit contains fructose and has many vitamins despite containing simple carbohydrates but table sugar, which has been refined, has been stripped of its vitamins and minerals.

Table 7.2   Nutritional value of mono- and disaccharides in different states

State of nutrient	Refined	Unrefined
Sources	Sweets and confectionary Table sugar Soft drinks Chocolate bars Cakes and biscuits Preserves	Fruit Fruit juices and smoothies Milk Yoghurt
Nutrient yield	Energy	Energy Vitamins Minerals Fibre

Spotlight: Fruit juice and smoothies – good nutritional choices or just sources of sugar?

Fruit juices and smoothies are coming under close inspection at present as they are sources of large amounts of 'sugar'. However, the sugar is mainly in the form of fructose, which has a much lower impact on blood glucose levels than glucose found in sweets, fizzy drinks and biscuits. Also, fruit juice and smoothies contain high levels of vitamins and minerals, absent in traditional snack foods.

What fruit juice and smoothies are missing is the fibre that occurs naturally in fruit. Fibre is found in the skin and core of fruits such as apples, as well as surrounding individual segments of citrus fruits such as oranges. Fibre has many roles and it makes us feel full as well as slowing down how quickly we can eat a food. While we can consume the juice of six to eight oranges in one sitting, it would be difficult to consume more than two oranges at the same time. As a result, more fructose is made available in a fruit juice or smoothie than in the original fruit.

Fruit juice and smoothies that are free from any additional ingredients or made from concentrates are still good nutritional choices; however, eating the original fruit would be an even better choice.

Key point: Mono- and disaccharides

Monosaccharides are one unit of a sugar. Glucose, fructose and galactose are the monosaccharides.

Disaccharides are two units of sugar joined by a bond. Sucrose, lactose and maltose are the disaccharides.

► Oligosaccharides

The term 'oligo' means 'few', and oligosaccharides are made up of chains of three to nine monosaccharides. They are present in vegetables such as peas and beans and in lentils.

► Polysaccharides

The term 'poly' means 'many' and, as shown in Figure 7.1, polysaccharides are made up of chains linking 10 or more (up to thousands) of monosaccharides with bonds. They are often referred to as 'complex carbohydrates' as they form complex structures.

Complex carbohydrates are often regarded as 'good' carbohydrates but again their nutritional value depends on whether they have been refined or remain unrefined and in their natural state. An athlete could follow advice to base their diet on complex carbohydrates but still eat a relatively unhealthy diet if they based it on refined products. Examples of refined and unrefined carbohydrates are shown in Table 7.3.

Table 7.3 Nutritional value of polysaccharides in different states

State of nutrient	Refined	Unrefined
Sources	White bread White pasta White rice Cakes and biscuits Breakfast cereals – corn flakes, rice crispies	Wholemeal/wholegrain bread Wholegrain rice Wholegrain pasta Muesli Porridge oats Potatoes, sweet potatoes
Nutrient yield	Energy Protein	Energy Protein Vitamins Minerals Fibre

Monosaccharides
- Glucose
- Fructose
- Galactose

Disaccharides
- Sucrose = glucose + fructose
- Lactose = glucose + galactose
- Maltose = glucose + glucose

Polysaccharides

10 or more glucose molecules

Figure 7.1 The structure of saccharides

Spotlight: Brown products – a good source of carbohydrate?

The difference between 'white' carbohydrate products and 'brown' carbohydrate products is that the white products have been stripped of the majority of their nutrients and so represent poorer nutritional choices.

Brown products take longer to prepare and generally take longer to chew and consume as their fibre content makes them harder to digest. However, this is a benefit, as it slows down how quickly we eat and makes us more likely to stop when we feel full. Some people complain that they don't like the taste of brown products as much as white products but this is often a reflection of which foods they have become used to. It can take three to four weeks to re-educate the palate to favour brown products over white products.

Brown products have the benefit of taking longer to digest and releasing glucose into the bloodstream more slowly owing to their fibre content. They provide additional nutrients needed in energy production and for health. As a result they represent a good choice for athletes and for people interested in eating healthily.

Key point: Oligo- and polysaccharides

Oligosaccharides are chains of a few (3–9) monosaccharides.

Polysaccharides are chains of 10+ monosaccharides.

GLYCAEMIC INDEX

Glycaemic index is a ranking of foods from 0–100 according to how quickly a carbohydrate food is broken down and enters the bloodstream as glucose. All carbohydrates end up as glucose and raise blood glucose levels, and glycaemic index is a measure of the effect a carbohydrate food has on blood glucose levels. Glucose has a glycaemic index (GI) of 100 and all other foods are compared to this standard. An index of 85–100 is regarded as high GI, 60–84 as moderate GI, and less than 60 as low GI.

A food with a high GI results in glucose quickly entering the bloodstream and causing a high spike in blood glucose levels. When blood glucose levels rise, the pancreas is stimulated to release insulin to lower the blood glucose level. Insulin is a hormone that allows glucose to flow into the cells of the muscle and liver with a resulting fall in blood glucose levels. If blood glucose has risen quickly, it will produce a high insulin response, causing the pancreas to release large quantities of insulin into the bloodstream. Moderate and low GI foods release their glucose into the bloodstream more slowly, so the pancreas releases insulin over a longer period of time and is placed under less strain.

Because high GI foods release energy quickly they make the individual feel energized, but as insulin causes blood glucose levels to fall the individual will start to feel tired and lethargic because the glucose supply to brain is reduced. Often the response to this is to consume another high GI food to boost blood glucose levels, and this leads to a cycle where blood glucose levels never stabilize. Historically, we have relied on low GI foods that release glucose slowly over a long period of time, meaning we avoid energy peaks and troughs.

The GI of a carbohydrate food, as shown in Table 7.4, depends on several factors. The presence of fibre, protein and fat lowers the GI, while processing and cooking raises it. The type of saccharides present in the food also have an impact; fructose and lactose have to go to the liver to be broken down, which results in their glucose being fed into the bloodstream much more slowly.

Table 7.4 The glycaemic index of common carbohydrate foods (adapted from Bean, 2013, pp. 289–91)

High GI	Moderate GI	Low GI
Glucose 100	Cornflakes 81	Fructose 20
Parsnips 97	Chips 75	Bananas 52
French baguette 95	Watermelon 72	White pasta 50
Honey 87	White bread 70	Porridge oats 49
Baked potato 85	White rice 64	Cherries 22

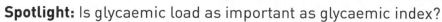

Spotlight: Is glycaemic load as important as glycaemic index?

Glycaemic load (GL) measures the total amount of carbohydrate available in a food as well as its glycaemic index. It is calculated by multiplying the carbohydrate available by its glycaemic index. GL is important because it offers an indication of the food's effect on blood glucose and insulin levels.

A high glycaemic load can result from eating a small amount of a high GI food or a large amount of a low GI food. While it is advisable to limit high GI foods, it is also advisable to limit high GL foods or meals with a high GL as they can lead to long-term health problems.

Key point: Glycaemic index (GI)

Glycaemic index rates how quickly a carbohydrate food is broken down into glucose and enters the bloodstream.

Proteins

Proteins are a component of every cell of the body and are needed to repair any damaged cells and to promote growth. Structural proteins form structures such as muscle, bone, skin, cartilage, hair and nails. Functional proteins are found in the form of hormones, enzymes and lipoproteins. In the body most of the protein is found as actin and myosin, which are muscle proteins.

Just as the smallest unit of a carbohydrate is glucose, the smallest unit of a protein is an amino acid. When we eat a protein food, it is broken down into amino acids in the small intestine and these individual amino acids are delivered to the liver and then sent to cells to be rebuilt into proteins. There are 20 amino acids that can be used to make proteins in the body (McArdle, Katch and Katch, 2013). There are around 50,000 different structures in the body that are made up of long chains of amino acids. The definition of a protein is a chain of up to 100 amino acids (McArdle, Katch and Katch, 2013), which is also referred to as a polypeptide. To make up structures of the body, hundreds or thousands of proteins are linked together.

The 20 amino acids available to make proteins include eight essential amino acids (Bean, 2013; Kreider, 2011) or nine essential amino acids for babies and children (Kreider, 2011). An 'essential' amino acid is one that must be gained in the diet. The other 12 amino acids are referred to as 'non-essential' because they can be made in the liver if all eight essential amino acids are in plentiful supply in the diet. The essential and non-essential amino acids are shown in Table 7.5.

SOURCES OF PROTEIN

Sources of protein include red meat, poultry, eggs, fish, milk and beans. Sources are divided into two categories, complete and incomplete:

▶ a complete protein food is one that provides sufficient amounts of all eight essential amino acids

▶ an incomplete protein food is one which is missing one or more of the essential amino acids.

Table 7.5 Essential and non-essential amino acids

Essential amino acids	Non-essential amino acids
Isoleucine	Alanine
Leucine	Arginine
Lysine	Asparagine
Methionine	Aspartic acid
Phenylalanine	Cysteine
Threonine	Glutamic acid
Tryptophan	Glutamine
Valine	Glycine
	Histidine*
	Proline
	Serine
	Tyrosine

* Histidine is an essential amino acid for babies and children but not adults.

The biological value of a protein rates a food in reference to the amounts of each essential amino acid it contains. For example, eggs are the most protein-complete food and have a biological value of 100, i.e. an egg has high amounts of all eight essential amino acids. In comparison, soya beans have a biological value of 47 as they just about have sufficient amounts of each essential amino acid to be regarded as complete. Table 7.6 separates foods into sources of complete and incomplete proteins and shows the biological value of selected protein foods.

Table 7.6 Sources of complete and incomplete protein and their biological value

Sources of complete protein (and their biological value)	Sources of incomplete protein (and their biological value)
Egg (100)	Wheat (44)
Fish (70)	Peanut (43)
Poultry (69)	Bean (34)
Beef (69)	Potato (34)
Dairy/Milk (60)	
Soya bean (47)	

A carnivorous diet is very likely to meet the protein needs of an individual but a vegetarian or vegan diet is also capable of providing all eight essential amino acids. A vegetarian can rely on dairy products, such as cheese, milk, yoghurt and soya beans, while a vegan needs a wide range of foods containing protein. They would use complementary protein or protein-partnering, where two or more foods containing incomplete sources of protein are eaten together. For example, wheat and beans or beans on toast would provide adequate amounts of each essential amino acid to enable the liver to synthesize the 12 non-essential amino acids.

Key point: Amino acids

Amino acids are the smallest unit of a protein. All proteins are eventually broken down into their individual amino acids.

There are eight essential amino acids, which must be gained from the diet, and 12 non-essential amino acids that can be synthesized if all eight essential amino acids are present in the diet.

PROTEIN REQUIREMENTS FOR ATHLETES

A sedentary person requires 0.8 grams of protein per kilogram of their body weight every day; if they weighed 70 kilograms, they would require an intake of 56 grams of protein per day. However, exercise is catabolic on muscle proteins, meaning that it breaks down muscle proteins, so active people have an increased demand for protein. The amount of damage accrued by muscle and other structures of the body is linked to the intensity of exercise; athletes involved in strength or anaerobic training have greater demands than those involved in aerobic endurance training.

Athletes involved in endurance exercise are recommended an intake of 1.2–1.8 g/kg/day (Jeukendrup and Gleeson, 2010) while strength athletes should aim for 1.6–1.7 g/kg/day (Jeukendrup and Gleeson, 2010). Hypertrophy, or athletes seeking to develop muscle, should aim for between 1.8–2.0 g/kg/day (Bean, 2013). The recommended amount of protein that should be consumed at each sitting is between 15–25 g (Phillips and van Loon, 2011). Protein is best taken in smaller, regular meals as the liver can only deal with small amounts at any time and any excess protein will either be excreted or stored as fat.

Fats

Fats are also called 'lipids' and the smallest unit of a fat is a fatty acid. These are packaged in the diet as triglycerides or triacylglycerides and they are structured as three fatty acids attached to a glycerol background, as seen in Figure 7.2. Figure 7.2 (a) shows a triglyceride with three fatty acids attached to the glycerol backbone; in order to be used as energy, the fatty acids need to detach from the glycerol backbone (b) and enter the bloodstream to be taken to whereever they are needed for energy production.

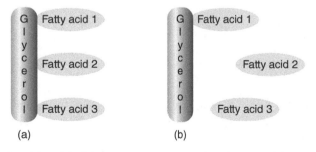

Figure 7.2 Structure of a triglyceride: (a) attached to the glycerol background, (b) detaching from the glycerol background

Triglycerides are present in foods containing fats and oils, such as meat, fish, poultry and dairy products, or in foods fried in fats and oils. Fats are often regarded as undesirable in our diets as they have been linked to obesity and heart disease, but recently the thinking about fats has changed and they are now divided into 'good' fats (such as butter, coconut oil and olive oil), which are naturally occurring, and 'bad' fats (found in deep fried foods, processed foods and in spreads) that have been processed or altered in some way. Fats perform the following important functions in the body that are essential to our health:

▶ the formation of virtually all cell membranes

▶ the formation of the myelin sheaths that coat nerves

▶ the production of steroid hormones

- provide a fuel source during low-intensity exercise

- the transportation, storage and utilization of fat-soluble vitamins A, D, E and K

- the production of heat

- the protection of internal organs.

> **Key point:** Fatty acids
>
> Fatty acids are the smallest unit of a fat and are packaged in the diet as triglycerides, which are three fatty acids attached to a glycerol backbone.

SATURATED AND UNSATURATED FATTY ACIDS

Fatty acids consist of chains of carbon atoms with hydrogen atoms attached. There is a methyl group (CH_3) at one end and an acid group (COOH) at the other end. This structure can be seen in Figure 7.3. Fatty acids have carbon chains of different lengths, varying from as few as four carbon atoms in a chain up to chains of more than 20 carbon atoms. Chain lengths of 16 and 18 carbons (long chain fatty acids) are most common.

The different lengths of carbon chains as well as whether they are saturated or unsaturated account for the differences in the many types of fat available. Animal fat, butter, lard, ghee, olive oil, safflower oil, avocado oil and sunflower oil are all types of fat but they differ in their colour, consistency, taste and texture because the fatty acids differ in length and structure.

▶ Saturated fatty acids

A saturated fatty acid is one in which all atoms in the carbon chain are attached to hydrogen atoms or they are holding as many hydrogen atoms as is chemically possible (McArdle, Katch and Katch, 2013). Figure 7.3 shows the chain of carbon atoms (C) where all carbon atoms have four bonds, each one represented by a line (—). There are equal numbers of hydrogen atoms above and below the carbon chain.

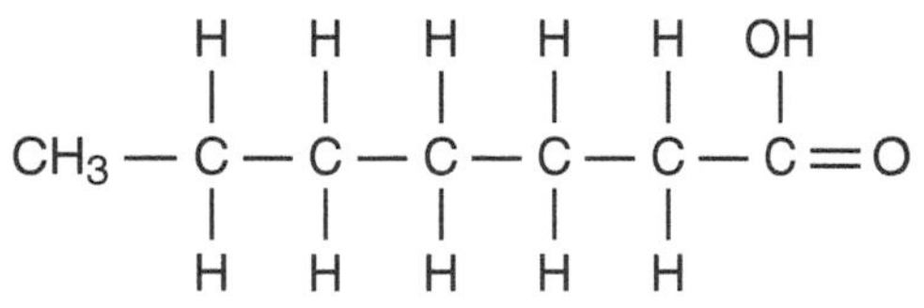

Figure 7.3 A saturated fatty acid

Saturated fatty acids occur in animal products such as beef, lamb, pork, egg yolks, cheese and cream. There are some plant sources of saturated acids, such as coconut oil and palm oil. Saturated fats are solid at room temperature and are chemically stable. This means that their structure does not change irrespective of what is done to them, particularly when heat is applied to them.

▶ Monounsaturated fatty acids

Unsaturated fats are produced when there is one double bond in the carbon chain. This is shown in Figure 7.4, where the second and third carbons are joined by a double bond (=). These fatty acids are created when there is a shortage of hydrogen atoms available and because carbon atoms must have four bonds, two of the carbon atoms form a double bond with each other.

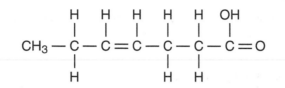

Figure 7.4 A monounsaturated fatty acid

Monounsaturated fatty acids are present in olives, peanuts, avocados and almonds and their oils. In their oil form they tend to be viscous liquids at room temperature but become thinner if heat is applied. Because of the presence of the double bond, monounsaturated fatty acids are less stable or more reactive than saturated fatty acids.

▶ Polyunsaturated fatty acids

Polyunsaturated fatty acids are produced when there are many double bonds in the carbon chain. Figure 7.5 shows a fatty acid with two double bonds. Carbon atoms are only joined to each other because there is a shortage of hydrogen atoms but these double bonds make them unstable or highly reactive. This means that if the conditions they are in change, such as when heat, oxygen or hydrogen is added, their structure starts to change.

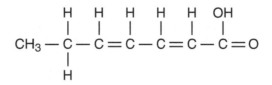

Figure 7.5 A polyunsaturated fatty acid

Polyunsaturated fatty acids are found in corn, oily fish, nuts, and sunflower seeds and its associated oil. Naturally occurring polyunsaturated fats, such as Omega-3 oils found in salmon and herrings, can have a beneficial effect on health. They are associated with a decreased incidence of heart disease, lower lipid content in the blood and reduced inflammation in the body (McArdle, Katch and Katch, 2013).

Spotlight: Hydrogenated vegetable oils and trans fatty acids

While unsaturated fatty acids in their natural form are associated with health benefits, their structure can easily be changed by processing or heating. The food industry uses a process called 'hydrogenation', in which an unsaturated fatty acid is heated to extremely high temperatures and then hydrogen is added at a very high pressure in the presence of a nickel catalyst.

This process causes the double bonds in the unsaturated fatty acids to be broken, and the addition of hydrogen results in the formation of saturated fats as the hydrogen attaches to these now-available bonds. Once the liquid has cooled down, a hard, waxy substance is produced. This is referred to as 'hydrogenated vegetable oil' and its appearance is not unlike that of a saturated fatty acid. Some of these processed fatty acids will be trans fatty acids, which are formed when hydrogen atoms move to the opposite side of the carbon chain, causing changes in its structure.

Hydrogenation is a way of manufacturing cheap 'solid' fats that can be used instead of more expensive solid fats like butter. They are found in products such as pastries, biscuits, margarines, pre-prepared foods and pies. They are linked to premature heart disease, with Willett and Ascherio (1994) reporting that 30,000 premature deaths a year were attributed to the consumption of trans fatty acids. A study of over 84,000 women in the USA linked diets high in trans fatty acids to increased insulin resistance and an increased risk of type 2 diabetes (McArdle, Katch and Katch, 2013).

In recent years the major supermarkets have stated their intention of eliminating all trans fatty acids from foods. One of the major supermarkets has banned trans fatty acids from all of its own brand products. Reducing the amount of processed foods that you eat as well as limiting deep-fat fried foods is beneficial in lowering your trans fatty acid intake.

Summary of research: The association of saturated fat intake and heart disease

It had almost become accepted as a fact in nutrition that the increased prevalence of heart diseases, such as heart attacks, high blood pressure and strokes, were the result of high levels of saturated fat in our diets. The reason being that when you eat a high-fat food such as a beef burger with melted cheese it raises your blood cholesterol levels. The raised cholesterol causes arteries to become clogged and these clogged arteries cause heart attacks.

However, in 2010 Siri-Tarino et al. completed a meta-analysis of 21 research studies of the relationship between dietary saturated fat consumption and coronary heart disease (CHD), strokes and cardiovascular disease (CVD). From 21 studies they concluded that there is no significant evidence for a relationship between dietary saturated fat and CHD or CVD. In their discussion they suggested that the type of carbohydrate consumed to replace dietary fat is likely to be a more important dietary influence on CVD risk, although they said that the studies they had looked at provided insufficient evidence to support this.

In 2013, Aseem Malhotra presented a seminal article, 'Saturated fat is not the major issue', in the *British Medical Journal*. His aim was to demolish the myth of the role of saturated fat in heart disease. He explains how the nutrition advice currently provided is based on Ancel Key's 'seven countries' study in 1970. Keys showed that a correlation existed between the number of calories consumed as fat and the prevalence of CHD in seven countries. His graph clearly shows that the higher the level of saturated fat consumed, the greater the incidence of heart disease in a country.

One problem with Keys' study is that correlation does not show causation, i.e. because two things are related, one does not necessarily cause the other. For example, there is a correlation between ice cream sales and deaths by drowning because as one increases so does the other, but it does not mean that ice cream consumption increases your chances of death by drowning.

Another problem with Keys' study is that he had data from 16 more countries that he chose not to include in his study because they did not fit the pattern. The data showed that Finland and Mexico have the same fat intake but Mexicans have very low rates of heart disease and Finns very high rates.

One of the outcomes of Keys' findings is that in 1977 dietary recommendations were produced in the USA stating that a high-carbohydrate and low-fat diet was the healthiest way to eat. Saturated fat in diets in the USA has since decreased from 30–40 per cent with the introduction of low-fat foods. Unfortunately, fats with lower fat contents lose their taste so this is replaced by adding sugar and other additives to give the food colour, taste and texture. As fat intake has decreased, obesity has boomed; as of September 2014 over 50 per cent of Americans were classed as obese (Noakes, 2015).

Malhotra (2013) summarizes the current thinking by saying, 'The scientific evidence is mounting that sugar is the possible independent risk factor for metabolic syndrome'. Metabolic syndrome is characterized by fat storage in the waist area, high blood pressure and high blood triglyceride levels.

Vitamins and minerals

These micronutrients, although required in very small amounts, are vital for growth and metabolism. They enable our bodies to function correctly every day and enable processes that sustain life to occur. Each vitamin and mineral has its own function, as can be seen in Tables 7.7 and 7.8, but their primary role is to act together to catalyse the chemical reactions that support life.

Life is sustained by millions of chemical reactions occurring every day in our bodies; however, these chemical reactions are reliant on the action of enzymes that are described as being 'biological catalysts'. The role of a catalyst is to speed up chemical reactions in the body so that these occur quickly enough to sustain life. Enzymes can speed up chemical reactions by up to one million times. Enzymes themselves are activated by coenzymes, which are derived from vitamins, and cofactors, which are derived from minerals. In summary, vitamins and mineral play a key role in the function of enzymes which support life.

Vitamins and minerals are gained predominantly from fruit and vegetables but are also present in other foods, including eggs, meat, fish and pulses.

Spotlight: The role of vitamin B in sports performance

The family of B vitamins are very important as they are needed to convert glucose and fats into energy. Naturally occurring foods, such as bananas, are excellent sports foods because they provide carbohydrates in two forms: glucose that can be used for energy immediately, and fructose that will provide energy over a longer period of time. Crucially, these foods contain B vitamins, which means that the glucose available can be converted into energy.

Many sports drinks, gels and bars are cleverly designed to contain some fast-release carbohydrates, some moderate-release carbohydrates and some slow-release carbohydrates. They also contain B vitamins so that this energy becomes available to the working muscles.

Refined sugars, such as sweets and fizzy drinks, that are consumed without B vitamins need to rely on the body's store of B vitamins to make them available for energy. Hence they are often termed 'anti-nutrients'.

Vitamins are categorized as water-soluble or fat-soluble to describe how they are transported, stored and used in the body. Vitamins A, D, E and K are water-soluble, while vitamins B and C are fat-soluble. The main distinction between the two categories is that the body is better at storing fat-soluble vitamins and as a result water-soluble vitamins need to be consumed on a daily basis.

Table 7.7 Sources and functions of vitamins

Name	Source	Function
Vitamin A	Milk products, liver, mackerel	Vision, bone development
Vitamin B	Red meat, fish, poultry, eggs, nuts, beans	Energy production, red blood cell production
Vitamin C	Fruit, vegetables	Fighting infection, formation of collagen, antioxidant
Vitamin D	Sunlight, eggs, oily fish	Bone formation, absorption of calcium and phosphorous
Vitamin E	Nuts, grains, green leafy vegetables	Antioxidant, promotes growth and development
Vitamin K	Green leafy vegetables	Formation of blood clots

Table 7.8 Sources and functions of minerals

Name	Source	Function
Calcium	Milk, milk products, whole grains, cereals	Bone and teeth formation, muscle contraction
Magnesium	Nuts, green leafy vegetables, eggs	Nerve and muscular function, maintaining heart rhythm
Sodium	Shellfish, vegetables, bacon	Fluid balance (attracts water into cells)
Potassium	Citrus fruits, green leafy vegetables, bananas	Fluid balance (repels water from cells)
Zinc	Seafood, red meats, beans, nuts	Development of new cells, antioxidant
Iron	Red meat, liver, potatoes, beans	Production of haemoglobin

There is some controversy about whether it is beneficial to supplement athletes' diets with vitamin and mineral pills or powders. The general consensus is that it is preferable for an athlete to get their vitamins and minerals from traditional food sources, and if a varied diet is consumed supplementation is unnecessary. There has been a school of thought, often misguided, that says 'if a little is good, more must be better' and this led to supplements being recommended.

FREE RADICALS AND ANTIOXIDANTS

The one time that supplements may be recommended is antioxidant nutrients for aerobic athletes. Antioxidants are enzymes that limit the damage caused by free radicals. Free radicals are molecules with an unpaired electron. Most molecules have paired electrons and an unpaired electron makes them unstable so they try to steal an electron from other molecules. This causes damage to cells and is linked to heart disease and cancer (Bean, 2013). Unfortunately, oxygen produces free radicals that attack cells, nerves and joints and damage them. It is paradoxical that oxygen supports life but also contributes to killing us! The more oxygen that is taken in, the more damage that is caused. This is why aerobic athletes are particularly at risk.

The body is able to neutralize most free radicals, as long as we have plenty of fruit and vegetables in our diet. Vitamins A, C and E and the minerals zinc and selenium are referred to as the 'antioxidant nutrients' as they provide the greatest defence against free radical damage. Some nutritionists advise endurance aerobic athletes to take an antioxidant supplement as additional protection against free radicals.

Hydration

Because of the body's stores of fat, protein and carbohydrate, it is possible to survive for six to seven weeks without food. However, it is only possible to survive for two to three days without water. On a daily basis, 2 litres of water are lost through breathing, sweating and urine production. This can increase to 3 litres as a result of training, particularly if it is warm and the session lasts over an hour. Therefore we need to drink at least 2 litres of water a day, drinking at regular intervals throughout the day. The best advice is to take two or three sips of water every 15 minutes and to get into the habit of carrying a water bottle around with you.

Dehydration occurs when fluid loss exceeds fluid intake. Its signs and symptoms are:

▶ thirst

▶ dizziness

▶ headache

▶ dry mouth

▶ poor concentration

▶ flushed, red-coloured skin

▶ increased heart rate.

Dehydration is linked to a decrement in performance, as loss of over 3 per cent of body weight through fluids produces significant reductions in aerobic power (Webster et al., 1990). Dehydration, or hypo-hydration, causes a loss of blood plasma and increasing viscosity of the blood. This in turn slows down blood flow, increases blood pressure and reduces the ability to sweat.

Hyper-hydration is when an athlete takes on extra water prior to exercising in a hot environment to minimize the onset of dehydration. The athlete does this by drinking steadily for 24 hours prior to the event and then drinking 500 ml about 20 minutes before the event starts. Then they will need to continually top up during the event.

FLUID INTAKE

Athletes, particularly aerobic athletes, are advised to consume 2.5–3 litres of water a day to replenish the losses during exercise. During an event they should continually top up their fluid levels to compensate for fluid lost as sweat.

Water is a always a good choice of fluid but it is best consumed at room temperature, as then it passes through the stomach more quickly. Cold drinks have to be brought up to the internal body temperature before leaving the stomach and so take longer to be available to muscles.

Spotlight: Choices of sports drinks

Sports drinks have a benefit over water because they can provide energy in the form of carbohydrate as well as providing fluid replacement. However, there are different types of sports drinks:

Isotonic – these drinks are so-called because they have an equal concentration of dissolved solids as the blood and as a result they are absorbed very quickly. They contain 6 grams of carbohydrate per 100 ml of water and thus provide a good source of fuel and a good source for hydration. These drinks can be used before, during and after performance.

Hypotonic – these drinks have a lower concentration of solids than the blood and are absorbed even more quickly than isotonic drinks. They are very useful for maintaining hydration but as they only contain 2 grams of carbohydrate per 100 ml of water they provide relatively little fuel. They are often used post-exercise for rehydration, and as they are lower in calories they are often favoured by people aiming for weight loss.

Hypertonic – these drinks have a higher concentration of dissolved solids than blood and as a result are absorbed relatively slowly. They contain 10 grams of carbohydrate per 100 ml of water and provide an excellent source of energy but hydration occurs more slowly. They are useful as an energy boost pre-performance or during an event to keep fuel levels high.

Pre-, during and post-exercise nutrition

For athletes, the optimal diet will provide supplies of nutrients in adequate amounts so that they have the right amount of energy for their daily training, tissue maintenance, repair and growth. The aim is to improve performance, achieve maximum gains from training, maximize recovery and prevent injury. McArdle, Katch and Katch (2013) identify three key principles for a healthy diet:

▶ variety – choose a variety of foods so that all nutrients can be gained from foods; in particular, choose a variety of fruit and vegetables and foods of varied colours

▶ balance – foods should be chosen from all food groups so that all available nutrients can be accessed

▶ moderation – avoid over-indulging in one of the food groups and balance meals with a high proportion of one nutrient by limiting that nutrient at the next meal.

PRE-EXERCISE NUTRITION

There are three aims of the pre-exercise meal:

▶ to ensure glycogen stores are well-stocked

▶ to ensure blood glucose levels are stable

▶ to ensure the body is well hydrated.

This will ensure that the athlete feels energized and motivated for their training session or performance. It is best to avoid fats and proteins pre-exercise because they take a long time to be digested.

It is advisable to eat a meal two to four hours before exercise (Hargreaves et al., 2004). The meal should be carbohydrate-rich, with 150–300 grams in solid or liquid form (McArdle, Katch and Katch, 2013). It is also important to ensure that there are enough vitamins and minerals in the meal to allow glucose to be converted into energy. There is some controversy about whether carbohydrate should be high or low GI; based on the available evidence, Bean (2013) concludes that low GI meals produce a sustained source of glucose for the exercise to come.

Hypertrophy or anaerobic athletes may include some protein in their pre-exercise meal so that they have amino acids available to replace those damaged during training. It is also important to ensure optimal hydration by continually sipping water in the two hours before exercise.

DURING EXERCISE

Aerobic endurance exercise at a high intensity reduces glycogen stores by around 55 per cent an hour and after two hours they are fully depleted (McArdle, Katch and Katch, 2013). Therefore any athlete training or competing for more than an hour and a half is recommended to take on carbohydrates during performance. This is best consumed as a drink in which glucose can be dissolved but some athletes use sweets like jelly beans to provide glucose quickly. McArdle, Katch and Katch (2013) suggest that adding small amounts of protein can reduce time to fatigue at a ratio of roughly 3:1 in favour of carbohydrates.

POST-EXERCISE

The priority post-exercise is to replace the depleted glycogen stores and replace fluids lost through sweating. It is recommended that athletes start refuelling immediately after exercise has stopped. Glycogen storage is 150 per cent faster in the first two hours after exercise (Ivy et al., 1988), in what is described by athletes as a 'golden window'. Therefore it is important to eat carbohydrates as quickly as possible after finishing exercise. McArdle, Katch and Katch (2013) recommend 50–75 grams of high or moderate GI carbohydrates in the first 15 minutes after exercise and then another 50–75 grams in the next two hours. If glycogen stores have been completely depleted, it may be necessary to keep refuelling by eating additional amounts of 50–75 grams of carbohydrates every two hours. A hypertrophy or strength athlete should consume up to 30 grams of protein, as protein stimulates muscle synthesis and reduces muscle catabolism (Howarth et al., 2009).

Post-exercise it is easiest to consume sports drinks or sports bars and water as it is unlikely a meal will be available, although some athletes eat fresh fruit and yoghurt after exercise. Hypertrophy athletes often have a protein shake, as it provides them with amino acids that can be taken on very quickly. Protein shakes tend to made of whey protein that has high levels of branch chain amino acids (BCAAs) as these are heavily catabolized during exercise and need to be replaced.

Pre-exercise meals need to be experimented with, as foods have different impacts on different people. Some foods make you feel energized and some make you feel fatigued. If you arrive for training feeling fatigued or unmotivated, it may be that the pre-exercise meal is not appropriate. Some athletes find that fructose from fruit can cause stomach disturbances and is best avoided. Likewise, eating during an event needs to be practised because if something new is tried out during a competitive event it may have negative consequence for the athlete.

Summary of research: High-carbohydrate diets and endurance performance

Research into the impact of carbohydrates on performance has been conducted since the 1930s. The following is a famous quote from D.B. Dill, who conducted research into carbohydrates and performance: *'the ingestion of a heavy carbohydrate meal a few hours before the marathon race and a supply of glucose before and after the race are logical'*. It is quite a statement that these things are 'logical'! However, it was backed up with other research.

Christiansen and Hansen (1939) showed that athletes on low-carbohydrate diets reached exhaustion after 90 minutes, compared to those athletes on high-carbohydrate diets who reached exhaustion after 240 minutes.

Subsequent research in Scandinavia in the 1960s supported this. Scandinavian researchers developed muscle biopsy techniques in which they used a needle to remove a tiny portion of muscle tissue to assess its glycogen content. Bergstrom et al. (1967) demonstrated a clear link between muscle glycogen levels and submaximal exercise performance. They also demonstrated that a period of carbohydrate restriction followed by a few days of carbohydrate loading maximized muscle glycogen stores. Hence carbohydrate loading was developed so that in the week before a marathon the athlete had three days where no carbohydrate was eaten followed by three days of eating large amounts of carbohydrate.

High-carbohydrate diets for athletes gained credence through the 1970s and 1980s.

This 'logical conclusion' started to be questioned in the 2000s as none of the earlier studies had used placebo groups (groups who did not eat a high-carbohydrate diet). The only study that had a placebo group (Burke et al., 2000) showed that carbohydrate loading had no beneficial effect on performance.

This has led to studies into the impact of higher fat and lower carbohydrate diets for endurance exercise, as Volek et al. (2015) state that the effects of a high-carbohydrate diet are not uniform across all athletes and some athletes are experiencing benefits from adapting to high-fat diets.

Spotlight: Do low-carbohydrate and high-fat diets work for athletes?

The perceived wisdom concerning endurance performance and diet is that endurance athletes should eat a high-carbohydrate diet because carbohydrates are the only substrate that can provide energy to resynthesize ATP quickly enough; therefore, it is necessary to eat carbohydrates before exercise. However, the average 70 kg man with 15 per cent body fat stores around 135,000 kcal of energy as fat and 1600 kcal of energy as glycogen. So would it not make sense for our bodies to burn fat as a fuel, as it does when glycogen has run out, rather than carbohydrate?

Noakes et al. (2014) observe that there is no essential requirement to eat carbohydrates, as can be shown by the diets of dwellers in the Arctic and Antarctic, who have survived on animal fats, such as blubber, and have carbohydrate-free diets. Research conducted by Noakes in the 1980s showed that humans can adapt to this diet without any impairment in submaximal exercise performance.

Noakes (2014) reported on a meta-analysis of 11 studies into low-carbohydrate diets and endurance exercise over the past 31 years. Of these 11 studies, three showed that exercise performance improved in athletes following a high-fat diet, four were equivocal, two showed no effects and two showed a performance decrement. However, none of the studies involved 'fat-adapted athletes', that is, those athletes who have followed a high-fat diet for 6–12 months. So while much more research is needed, Noakes concluded that some athletes could produce the same performance after a period of fat adaptation.

The other concern about high-carbohydrate diets is the impact of a high consumption of sugar on health. A study by Schwartz et al. (2014) showed that marathon runners had a higher incidence of coronary artery disease than sedentary individuals. Malhotra et al. (2015) stated that there are growing concerns that athletes are at risk of developing type 2 diabetes as high-carbohydrate diets can produce increased insulin resistance.

Malhotra et al. (2015) recommended that athletes should avoid high-carbohydrate diets in favour of diets higher in fat because: *'fat, including ketone bodies, appears to be the ideal fuel for most exercise. It is abundant, does not need replacement or supplementation during exercise, and can fuel the forms of exercise in which most participate.'*

Summary

This chapter started with basic information about nutrition to provide a platform for understanding the more complex applications of this knowledge. Understanding what should be eaten for health and for performance can only be understood once the building blocks are in place.

There are many controversies in sports nutrition and in nutrition more generally. Every year we are exposed to new diets and new ways of eating, some of them sensible and others the result of misunderstanding or misinterpreting research. Nutrition is currently heavily researched and some snippets of this research that make their way into the media often lead to confusion and knee-jerk reactions.

That said, there is no doubt that this is a fascinating time to be studying sports nutrition as we seem to be entering a new era in understanding sports nutrition and performance.

Dig deeper

Online resources

Australian Sports Commission (Nutrition)
www.ausport.gov.au/ais/nutrition

British Nutrition Foundation
www.nutrition.org.uk

Canadian Centre for Ethics in Sport
www.cces.ca/sport-nutrition

Real Meal Revolution
http://realmealrevolution.com/

Science in Sport
www.scienceinsport.com/sports-nutrition

Books

A. Bean, *The Complete Guide to Sports Nutrition*, 7th edn (London: Bloomsbury, 2013).

L. Burke and G. Cox, *The Complete Guide to Food and Sports Performance* (Crows Nest, Australia: Allen and Unwin, 2007).

A. Jeukendrup and M. Gleeson, *Sports Nutrition: An introduction to energy production and performance*, 2nd edn (Champaign, IL: Human Kinetics, 2010).

W.D. McArdle, F.I. Katch and V.L. Katch, *Sports and Exercise Nutrition*, 4th edn (Baltimore, MD: Lippincott, Williams and Wilkins, 2013).

M.H. Williams, *Nutrition for Health, Fitness, and Sport* (New York: McGraw-Hill, 2007).

Fact-check

1 Which of the following are micronutrients?
  a Carbohydrates
  b Proteins
  c Fats
  d Vitamins

2 How many kcal does 1 gram of fat yield?
  a 0
  b 4
  c 7
  d 9

3 Which of the following sugars is a monosaccharide?
  a Fructose
  b Sucrose
  c Lactose
  d Maltose

4 Which of the following nutrients is provided by both refined and unrefined polysaccharides?
  a Vitamins
  b Minerals
  c Protein
  d Fibre

5 Which of the following foods would have a low GI?
  a Porridge oats
  b Honey
  c White bread
  d Baked potato

6 Which of the following is a source of incomplete protein?
  a Eggs
  b Wheat
  c Milk
  d Soya beans

7 What is the recommended protein intake for a hypertrophy athlete?
  a 0.75 g/kg/day
  b 1.2–1.8 g/kg/day
  c 1.6–1.7 g/kg/day
  d 1.8–2.0 g/kg/day

8 Which of the following is an example of a monounsaturated fat?
  a Olive oil
  b Sunflower oil
  c Coconut oil
  d Animal fat

9 Which of the following are antioxidant nutrients?

   a   Vitamins A, D, E and K

   b   Vitamins B and D

   c   Vitamins A, C and E

   d   Vitamins A, D and F

10 How much carbohydrate is it advisable to consume immediately after exercise?

   a   25–50 g

   b   50–75 g

   c   75–100 g

   d   150–175 g

Planning research in sport

As discussed in the introduction, research is central to building up a body of knowledge in a subject. It is how knowledge is gained and then shared with a wider community. Students are required to produce an independent piece of research, usually in the third year of an undergraduate degree programme. For some this is a daunting prospect, while others see it as an exciting opportunity to examine something of interest that they want to discover more about. The more you know about research and its value, the more relaxed you will be about tacking your own research project. Students studying for a Master's degree become more involved in research, while a PhD is almost entirely based on conducting research and writing up findings.

The purpose of research

Research is concerned with asking questions and attempting to answer them in a logical and systematic way. Research aims to develop knowledge in a subject area but, importantly, it also must be applicable to real-life situations so that it informs the practice of professionals working in sport. Gaining knowledge is often easier than implementing it in practice. While research can help present answers to a problem, it can often throw up more questions that need to be answered, or what is referred to as 'problem creating'. Burton and Bartlett (2005) summarized the purpose of research as:

▶ to advance our knowledge of a subject

▶ to make sense of the world

▶ to solve practical problems

▶ to underpin practice

▶ to stimulate further research.

> *'Those who are enamoured of practice without science are like a pilot who gets into a ship without rudder or compass and never has any certainty of where they are going.'*
> Leonardo da Vinci (1452–1519), Italian, painter, sculptor, architect and engineer

The process of research

The process of research starts with the researcher deciding what question they are going to ask. They then go through a process of research, or cycle of enquiry, as shown in Figure 8.1.

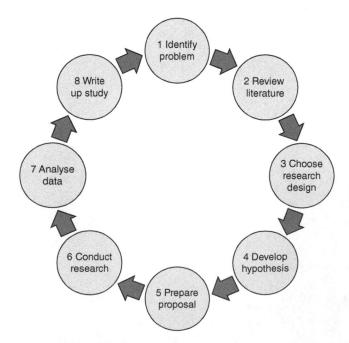

Figure 8.1 The process of research (Thatcher and Day, 2009)

Once the problem has been identified, the researcher looks at the existing body of literature and reviews what has already been found out as the result of similar studies. This gives the research its academic basis and although the research focus will be slightly different, it gives a researcher something to compare their results to. For example, the researcher may be looking at the effect of core training in golfers and they will be able to compare their results to the effect of core training in footballers.

The third stage is to design how the research will be conducted. This would include looking at:

▶ who will be in the sample (what level the golfers are playing at)

▶ how many will be in the sample

▶ what are they going to be compared to.

In our example of the effect of core training for golfers, the researcher may compare their performance before and after the core training or they may select one group to perform core training and a second group to not perform any core training. At this point the method of research would be decided. There are several different research instruments that can be utilized apart from the use of an experiment in this example. A researcher could also use questionnaires, interviews or observations to gather information. Each of these methods has benefits and disadvantages, which are examined in a later section.

The fourth stage is to develop the hypothesis, which is a statement of what the researcher expects to find in their study. It is often called the 'research hypothesis' and the researcher also develops an alternative or 'null hypothesis', which is the opposite of what they expect to find. For example:

▶ Research hypothesis: Core training techniques will lead to an improvement in performance at golf.

▶ Null hypothesis: Core training techniques will not lead to an improvement in performance at golf.

When writing up the study, researchers only refer to the research hypothesis unless they fail to prove it and then they would accept the null hypothesis.

Key point: Hypotheses

The hypothesis is the phenomenon that is being tested. The research, or experimental hypothesis, is what the researcher expects to find. The null hypothesis is the opposite of what they expect to find.

The fifth stage is to prepare a project proposal. This includes information such as: the title of the research, the aims and rationale, the proposed methodology, a description of the participants and the expected outcomes of the research. While this is important in the planning stage, its real importance is that this information needs to be supplied to an ethics panel. The ethics panel will review the proposal and ask whether it is ethical to research your proposed area. This would be of major concern if you were introducing a drug to people or using animals in research. In any research where you are trying out a new method of training, whether it is physical or psychological, there is the risk that it may result in harm to the participants. The ethics panel needs to be convinced that your research is safe and morally appropriate.

The sixth stage is to conduct your research once the proposal has been approved or amended for approval.

The seventh stage is conducted once results have been obtained and the data can be analysed. This usually relies on the use of statistical tests to examine whether any differences you have found in your research groups are statistically significant rather than due to chance.

The eighth and final stage is the small matter of writing up the research project within the required word count. An undergraduate dissertation is usually between 8000–10,000 words, and a Master's dissertation usually around 20,000 words. A PhD thesis is usually around 80,000 words, although it often results in a series of three or four journal articles being published as well.

Developing research questions

Unfortunately, as Miles and Huberman (1994) observed, *'You cannot study everyone, everywhere doing everything'*, so decisions have to be made about what is going to be researched. When developing the research question the researcher needs to consider two main things:

▶ What other factors may affect the results?

▶ What problems may need to be faced in the research?

Consider a piece of psychology research where the researcher wanted to research the following question: 'Can high levels of stress be a causative factor in the prevalence of injury?'

The first thing a researcher needs to consider is how they are going to measure stress and how they are going to measure the prevalence of injury. Stress is usually measured using a questionnaire, but when should the questionnaire be administered? How can we tell whether the injury was the result of the stress or of something else, such as a muscle weakness or the actions of an opponent? Also, what constitutes an injury? Would we consider cuts and bruises or are we talking about muscle injuries and damaged limbs?

'Variables' is the term used by a researcher to describe any factor that may affect results. In this example, stress is the variable that is being manipulated as the researcher may compare an athlete who has recorded a high score in the test to those who have recorded low scores in the test. However, there are many other variables that may not be controllable. Other factors that could cause injury would be environmental conditions, such as the state of the playing surface and the weather conditions, the actions of other people and the athlete's level of conditioning.

Key point: Variables

A variable is any factor that may change. The researcher is testing a variable as they want to see how it changes. However, other variables may affect results if they are not controlled.

It may be difficult to research athletes in a sport where there are variables that cannot be controlled. For example, the causes of injury in rugby are numerous and impossible to control.

However, if you were to research gymnasts completing their routines in a closed environment, or 100 metre sprinters, there would be fewer variables to control and injuries owing to the stress levels of the performer may be more accurately recorded.

Spotlight: Validity, objectivity and reliability

To anyone studying sports science the words 'validity', 'objectivity' and 'reliability' will become all too familiar as they are central to the credibility of any research, experiment or test that is conducted. These three measures must always be considered but although simple terms to define, they are much more difficult to implement:

▶ Validity – does the test actually measure what you say you are measuring (or is measuring something else)?

▶ Objectivity – is the test free from personal bias and opinion?

▶ Reliability – if this test were repeated, would it produce the same results?

To make a test valid, as many variables as possible must be controlled so that the one being manipulated is the one that is causing the change to happen.

Objectivity is difficult to achieve because most researchers are conducting the research to prove something that they believe to be important or to exist. As they are keen to prove something, they may be tempted to increase its chances of actually happening!

A reliable test is one which, if it was conducted by a different researcher, on a different day or at different time of the day, would yield the same results. Unfortunately, the performance of human beings is dependent on their mood or psychological state, their nutritional status, the amount of sleep they have had and the exercise they taken, as well as other factors such as the type of competition they are facing. Most of these factors influence the performance of the subject and the researcher as well.

In other words, research is fraught with problems! This chapter aims to guide you towards making good decisions with regard to any research or testing you may undertake.

Quantitative and qualitative research

The approach a researcher takes is known as their **methodology** and it can yield results that are expressed numerically, as a quantity (quantitative) or as views and opinions (qualitative). Very broadly speaking, most scientific research uses a quantitative methodology while research in social sciences uses a qualitative methodology. Experiments and questionnaires using scales of measurement produce quantitative data, while research using observation and open question interviews is likely to produce qualitative results. The different characteristics are set out in Table 8.1.

Table 8.1 Characteristics of quantitative and qualitative research

Characteristic	Quantitative research	Qualitative research
Type of data gathered	Information is in the form of numbers that are used to present findings as 'facts'	Information is presented as opinions or viewpoints and arguments from which the researcher extracts meaning and understanding. It often relates to thoughts, feelings or experiences
How data is analysed	Statistical analyses are used to determine causal relationships	Researchers look for patterns within the information and recurring words, phrases or opinions
Application of results	The researcher is aiming to produce unbiased results that can be generalized to a wider population	Small samples are used to examine why and how things are happening. Often used to inform decision making
Type of information gained	Information is objective but often lacks depth	Information can be subjective but is rich in quality
Where information is gained	The environment is often set up to enable information to be gathered	Information is often gained from a natural or real setting
Examples of research methods	Experiments Questionnaires	Participant research Open interviews Observation Surveys

Research methods

Once a researcher has developed their research question and decided on their experimental hypothesis, they have to decide which method is best suited to collecting the data. These are often referred to as research instruments or research tools.

QUANTITATIVE TECHNIQUES

▶ Experiments

Experiments can take the form of either laboratory-based or field-based data collection.

Laboratory-based tests are conducted in a closed environment that helps to control many variables. It means that factors such as temperature and humidity can be maintained at a constant level. The outcome of this is that there are fewer factors that can affect the validity and reliability of results. Laboratory-based tests are useful to assess physical measures of fitness as variables such as the intensity of exercise and the athlete's heart rate and breathing rate can be measured easily. Any equipment that is required, such as gas analysers or equipment to extract blood, can be kept close by and used properly. The environment is one that is free from the distraction that might be provided by the presence of other athletes or spectators.

Laboratory-based tests are able to provide valid and reliable information away from sporting environments. However, this strength is also their weakness: sport is played in field-based settings, not laboratories. Field-based tests can reproduce sporting environments more accurately and thus may be favoured by coaches. For example, an athletics coach would gain more useful information about the speed of their athletes in a race by testing them on an athletics track than on a treadmill. However, results gained in the field may be affected by external factors, such as wind and rain, conditions underfoot and the type of footwear the athletes are wearing.

▶ Questionnaires

The design of a questionnaire influences whether it elicits quantitative or qualitative data. Quantitative information is gained if the questions are closed and have a limited number of answers to choose from. Qualitative information is gained if the questions are open and there is no list of potential answers to choose from.

Closed questions can be answered in different ways. A simple yes/no question is unlikely to produce information of any depth or subtlety; however, they are useful in finding out information that is purely factual, like whether an individual has been skiing or taken exercise in the past week. Most questionnaires use a scale or a number of choices of answer. Likert scales, which make an individual rate themselves in relation to a question, are popular. An example of an item using a Likert scale is shown below:

Question: Choose one of the options in response to the following statement.

Footballers who dive to gain a penalty should receive an automatic one-match ban.

1 Strongly disagree

2 Disagree

3 Neither agree nor disagree

4 Agree

5 Strongly agree

Designing a questionnaire requires a lot of skill and the questions need to be constantly reviewed to ensure they are not biased or leading the respondent towards a certain answer. It is best to trial the questionnaire in a small pilot study before using it as a research instrument to ensure it is performing the way the researcher wants it to perform. Questionnaires can be a very effective research instrument as they can gain information from a large population in a relatively cheap way; they can also be relatively easy to analyse and extract the data they produce.

QUALITATIVE METHODS

▶ Interviews

The difference between a questionnaire and an interview is that the researcher is more active in the process of conducting the research. When using questionnaires, the researcher's activity may be restricted to distributing and collecting them. However, in an interview situation, they are conducting the interview and asking the questions themselves. This makes interviews a more time-consuming method, but if the researcher is able to establish trust and rapport with the respondent, they can produce information of a greater quality and depth than a questionnaire.

In an interview the questions should be open-ended, but the researcher has the opportunity to ask follow-up questions or to explore information the respondent supplies to them. Interviews of this type are referred to as semi-structured, because the researcher has prepared some questions beforehand but expects to develop more questions as the interview progresses.

▶ **Observations**

A certain type of information can be gained from observing behaviour as long as the researcher can remain free from bias. Observations are common in psychology to research how a person or team behaves in a certain situation or reacts to specific events. They are often used in conjunction with questionnaires or interviews; although questionnaires indicate what a person thinks they do, it can turn out that this is not always the case.

The behaviour of coaches or fitness trainers can be assessed using observation techniques. This type of observation can be made more reliable by the use of checklists. For example, the researcher may have a list of observable behaviours, such as what types of feedback a coach provides, to choose from. When the behaviour is present the researcher can tick the relevant box. This type of activity becomes more accurate when the observation is carried by more than one researcher. This is like judges in a boxing contest who are looking for specific actions to award points to and they use these points to decide which boxer wins each round. However, the boxer has to have been awarded the round by at least two of the judges, so they need to be recording the same actions.

Participant observation is a very specific method of observing behaviour. It occurs when the researcher becomes part of the group that they are observing. Because the population being researched are not aware that they are being observed, it increases the chances that they won't modify their behaviour as a response to being observed. This type of research was used to observe the behaviour of football hooligans to reach some understanding of their motives and the ways they operated. However, researching people who do not know they are being researched brings up some important ethical issues and as a result this research method has become less widely used.

Another specific type of observational study is a **longitudinal study** where people are observed over a long period of time. These are popular in psychology as they can track an individual's development over time, and in sociology where life events and their impact are studied. They often involve the use of diaries to record thoughts, feelings and events, and are useful in sports research to track issues such as career transitions into and out of sports, e.g. tracking an individual's thoughts about transitioning into retirement. These types of observational study can produce extremely useful information; however, they tend to be both time-consuming and fairly expensive.

Data analysis

The research, once conducted, will have produced what is described as 'raw data'. The researcher has a plethora of information but it is not organized or synthesized in any way. The aim of data analysis is to organize the data in a logical fashion to give it meaning in relation to the hypothesis the researcher is testing. Quantitative and qualitative data are analysed in different ways.

QUANTITATIVE DATA ANALYSIS

Quantitative data is best analysed using statistical tests. Some of these tests will be familiar to you and some you might be seeing for the first time.

'There are three kinds of lies: lies, damned lies and statistics.'
Benjamin Disraeli (1804–81), British statesman and novelist

Statistics are viewed with suspicion by some people as there is a perception that they can be used to present cases in the best or worst possible way. This is partly true in that the type of statistics are chosen to present information in the way that best backs up an argument. Statistics are really about describing observations in terms of numbers and making evaluations, or predictions, based on those observations. There are two types of statistics:

▶ Descriptive statistics – these allow the data collected to be described

▶ Inferential statistics – these identify whether a relationship or difference exists within the data and whether it is statistically significant.

In order for a study to gain coherence and credibility, the researcher should use both descriptive and inferential statistics.

Key point: Types of statistics

Descriptive statistics summarize the characteristics of a group, including the mean, mode, median, range and standard deviation.

Inferential statistics identify whether the results show that any relationships exist within a sample. Examples include correlations and tests of diference.

▶ Descriptive statistics

Sport is obsessed with descriptive statistics, from the most basic counts of how many shots a team have taken and what percentage of time they have had possession of the ball. In cricket we are concerned with the average score that a batsmen has recorded over a season rather than their individual scores in each match; indeed, the greatness of cricketers is determined by their batting average or the average number of runs they concede between taking wickets (bowling average). Journalists and commentators use statistics to make sense of sport. However, they do concede that sometimes the statistics do not tell the whole story. For example, the team with the greatest amount of possession is not necessarily the team most likely to win.

There are three commonly used measures of average, or what is referred to in statistics as 'measures of central tendency', as shown in Table 8.2.

Table 8.2   Measures of central tendency

Measure of central tendency	Description
Mean	The average score within a data set
Median	The number in the middle of the data set
Mode	The number most common in the data set

All three measures of central tendency are equally valid and often have different values. The researcher could choose the measure that best suits the outcome they desire so it is important to know which one is being used.

To get a better picture of a data set a researcher can use standard deviation. Standard deviation summarizes the variation, or dispersion, within a data set. Before looking at standard deviation, it is important to understand frequency distribution curves and what information they can present.

▶ Frequency distribution curves

Frequency distribution curves show how frequently particular scores are achieved in a data set. For example, if you were testing the intelligence of a population group you would choose a sample and then ask them to complete an IQ test. You would use the results to plot a frequency distribution curve and it would probably look like the curve in Figure 8.2. It is described as showing 'normal distribution'.

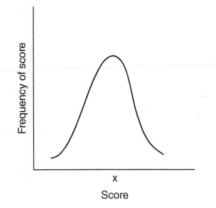

Figure 8.2 Frequency distribution curve

This normal distribution curve has three properties:

▶ the mean, median and mode occur at the same point

▶ it is 'bell-shaped' and has the same shape on both sides of the mean point

▶ the curve falls away from the mean point fairly slowly. This means that most scores are located close to the mean.

This normal distribution is not always found, as sometimes the distribution of scores can be skewed. This can be seen in Figure 8.3.

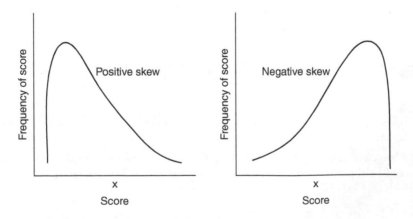

Figure 8.3 Skewed distribution curves

Skewed distributions are found where there is a small sample size or the sample selection is biased, e.g. if the sample included the IQs of a significant number of university students within a wider sample of the general population. Skewed samples may lead to less convincing results.

▶ Measures of dispersion

Dispersion describes the spread of the data or the variation between the scores. There are several measures of dispersion but we will focus on two, the range and the standard deviation. Below are sets of hypothetical scores for two batsmen in cricket over a series of eight innings, with their mean scores and range calculated.

Batsman 1: 1, 10, 25, 30, 40, 50, 65, 75. Mean = 37. Range = 74

Batsman 2: 34, 35, 36, 37, 37, 38, 39, 40. Mean = 37. Range = 6

The range is the difference between the highest and lowest scores but does it give a good description of the group? Probably not, because it only considers the two extreme scores, which in the case of Batsman 1 are considerably higher or lower than the rest. In this case the range does not give a good description of the group of scores. However, it does give a good description of the scores for Batsman 2.

Key point: Measures of dispersion

Measure of dispersion assesses how scattered the scores are in the sample or their variability.

Standard deviation is a more useful measure of dispersion as it measures how spread out the scores are in relation to the mean score. If standard deviation is high, then the scores are widely distributed with many scores occurring a long way from the mean. A small standard deviation means that most scores are close to the mean. Lower standard deviation scores are usually more desirable for a researcher who is trying to prove a relationship or show a trend. If the standard deviation is high, it shows that it is unlikely a strong relationship exists between two variables.

Spotlight: Regression to the mean

Cara and Becca are both experienced athletics coaches. Cara's coaching strategy is to heavily praise her athletes when they perform well and punish them with extra training when they perform poorly. However, it seems that her methods don't produce better performances than those of Becca's athletes, who receive neither praise nor punishment.

Cara asks Becca whether she thinks that praise or punishment works better in motivating athletes. Becca says it doesn't make any difference which one she uses. This was not the answer Cara wanted but is Becca right?

Becca is almost certainly right, because athletes' performances are subject to the phenomenon of 'regression to the mean'. This means than while some of the athletes' performances are excellent and some terrible, most of them are somewhere in the middle or close to the mean. It is almost inevitable that if a performance is excellent then the next one won't be so good, and if the performance is terrible the next one is likely to be better. So whether the athlete is rewarded or punished is irrelevant because over a period of time their results will be close to their mean, with a few excellent ones and a few terrible ones.

Regression to the mean is found everywhere and should be a source of optimism (and pessimism). For example, if your team plays badly and gets a bad result, it is likely that next time it will play better and get a better result; however, if the team plays well and gets a great result it is likely that in the next match it will regress to the mean and not produce such a good performance or result.

(Adapted from Ambridge (2014), pp. 53–5)

▶ Inferential statistics

Descriptive statistics are used to describe the data set but inferential statistics go a stage further and allow the researcher to determine whether there are relationships or significant differences in the data set. There are two types of inferential statistical tests.

- ▶ **Tests of association** – this is where the researcher wants to know if there is a relationship between two sets of variables. For example, whether height and swimming performance share a relationship. This relationship can be established by using a correlation test, such as Pearson's correlation or Spearman's correlation. These tests do the same thing but are based on different mathematical formulae. The closer the correlation score is to 1, the greater the relationship that exists between the two variables.

- ▶ **Tests of difference** – these tests tell us whether the results gained are statistically significant or were gained owing to chance. Researchers test two variables; for example, the effect of beetroot juice (variable 1) on endurance running performance (variable 2). If the result of the test is statistically significant, it means the result is probably not due to chance, but if it was not significant it is probable that it did occur due to chance. The level of significance is usually set at 5 per cent, so it means that there is only a 5 per cent chance that the results were due to chance.

In a set of data where a significant difference occurs, it means that if the test were repeated it would probably achieve the same results. The implication is that the test and the data set produced are reliable because it has been statistically proven. There are several statistical tests that researchers can use to establish differences. Different tests need to be used in different conditions.

- ▶ **Paired t-test** – If a test has involved the same sample of people repeating a test in two conditions, then a paired or related t-test is used. For example, the aerobic endurance of 50 subjects is tested before the sample have ingested beetroot juice and then again after they have ingested beetroot juice. It is the same sample group in two different conditions. Wilcoxon is an example of a paired t-test.

- ▶ **Unpaired t-test** – If a test involves two independent groups undergoing the same test, then an unpaired or unrelated t-test is used. For example, the aerobic endurance of a sample of 50 males who have ingested beetroot juice is compared to a sample of 50 females who have ingested beetroot juice. It is two different sample groups in one condition. Mann-Whitney U is an example of an unpaired t-test.

- ▶ **One-way ANOVA** – In some experiments there may be three sample groups or three experimental conditions. For example, the researcher may be looking at the effect of beetroot juice on the aerobic endurance of a sample of 20–29-year-olds, a sample of 30–39-year-olds and a sample of 40–49-year-olds. Alternately, the researcher may have three experimental conditions consisting of three different sized doses of beetroot juice. If either of these is the case, then a one-way ANOVA is the statistical test the researcher would employ.

QUALITATIVE DATA ANALYSIS

Once qualitative data has been collected the researcher will find that they have a lot of material in the form of observation records, notes, transcripts or diary entries. Lynch (2010) suggests four stages that can be followed to make sense of the data collected.

▶ 1 Organize the data

The data needs to be put into a workable format. Any audio recordings need to be turned into transcripts, videos need to be coded, notes need to be typed up, and observation checklists or records need to have their data collated.

▶ 2 Shape the data into information

This usually involves marking or coding the data into distinct themes or categories. This way the researcher can sift out the important information from the peripheral information. They may be looking for five or six themes and could colour code each theme or mark it differently in relation to the research questions. Once the information has been divided up into distinct themes, it may be possible to combine some of the themes.

▶ 3 Interpret and summarize the information

Now the researcher has to consider how to present the information so that it can be summarized. This may involve presenting different themes in different tables or the researcher may be able to utilize charts and graphs. At this point the researcher should be able to make summaries of the information. However, they need to be careful how these summaries are phrased. It is possible to say that 'some subjects said this' or 'other subjects said that' rather than referring to 'most', 'few' or even 'the majority' of subjects. It is important to ensure that all views and opinions drawn out in the research are accounted for in the summary.

▶ 4 Explain the information

Once the information has been analysed it needs to be explained. The researcher often chooses to discuss these findings with their peers so that they are able to reach appropriate conclusions and suggest how the results of the data can be used to inform practice.

Preparing and conducting research are skills that develop over time; there are many dangers and pitfalls for the researcher so they will make mistakes along the way. Often the mistakes offer information that is as valuable as the actual outcomes of the research study.

A useful gateway to starting your own research is to look at research that has already been completed and written up in the form of a journal article. Although these researchers have been published, they are sure to have faced many challenges during their research. Some of these challenges may have been overcome but there may still be weaknesses in their study that can be identified. The next section looks at how to read journal articles in a critical manner.

Reading journal articles critically

Journal articles are written in a very specific format. They are peer-reviewed by other specialists in the field to ensure their validity, objectivity and reliability and to highlight any issues. Journal articles typically have seven sections with the following titles and features.

- ▶ **Title:** The title describes the main area of research and the important variables.

- ▶ **Abstract:** The abstract is a brief summary of the entire article in around 120 words. It states the problem to be researched, the method employed, statistical tests used, the results and their implications. It is designed to allow the reader to decide whether the research is of interest to them and whether they want to keep on reading. It should not be treated as an alternative to reading the whole article.

- **Introduction:** The introduction is often the longest section and begins with stating the problem under investigation. The purpose of the introduction is to explain to the reader the problem being investigated and to justify this focus and the research hypothesis. This is done by reviewing research that has been done in the recent past in the same or similar research area. Referred to as the literature review, this often makes up a large bulk of the article.

- **Method:** The method describes the subjects in terms of their number, demographics (age, gender, education level, socio-economic status, etc.), any agreements made between the researcher and the subjects and any fees paid. It describes the materials used to conduct the research and provides a detailed account of the research method (experiment, interview or questionnaire). It should include enough detail for the research to be exactly replicated.

- **Results:** The results section presents the data gathered in both written and visual form and describes the outcomes of the statistical tests used to analyse the data.

- **Discussion:** The discussion section is used to summarize and review the results. The researcher then interprets and evaluates the results and describes how they fit with any previous research findings. The aim of the discussion is to come up with possible explanations or interpretations of the results. The discussion starts by restating the research hypotheses and then whether the research hypothesis has been accepted or rejected. It concludes with implications for future research and study.

- **References:** A full references list is provided as an alphabetical list of all the other works that have been referenced in the article. This is useful for the reader because if they want to find out more about previous research they can use these references to source the original articles.

WHAT TO LOOK OUT FOR WHEN READING CRITICALLY

The first three questions to ask about research are:

- Is the research valid?

- Is the research objective?

- Is the research reliable?

When judging the validity of an article it is important to look at how the author(s) have defined their terms and how they have controlled any variables that may affect their results. If they haven't controlled the variables, any one of these could be causing the outcome.

Objectivity can be assessed by looking at how the researcher presents their findings and whether the discussion is balanced between the two possible outcomes or hypotheses. It is always worth knowing who funded the research, as that can bias the research. A recent piece of published research found that cat owners were more intelligent than dog owners. On closer inspection it turned out that the research had been funded the charity Cats Protection! Nutritional research has been beset by problems of objectivity because it is often funded by manufacturers who are keen to prove that the claims they make about their product are backed up by scientific research.

When evaluating reliability you need to examine the method, as it should be described in enough detail for the research to be reproduced by another researcher using exactly the same methodology as the reported study. This is often a major flaw when types of training methods or massage techniques are being tested for a specific effect. It is often stated that 'training was conducted' or 'massage was applied', which gives no chance of the method being reproduced.

Other aspects you need to consider while critically reading journal articles include:

▶ How large is the sample?

▶ How has the sample been chosen?

▶ Is there a control group?

▶ What methods have they used – experimental testing, questionnaires, interviews?

▶ What have they done to prevent bias?

▶ How well-designed is the method; does it have any obvious flaws?

▶ How have they analysed the results?

▶ How have they presented the results (remember: 'lies, damned lies and statistics')?

▶ What is scientific fact and what is opinion?

▶ Have they presented their weaknesses to inform future research?

Control groups are often used in scientific experiments as they offer a baseline to which the researcher can compare their results. For example, if the research was into the effect of a cooling spray on injury recovery, the rescarcher may have two groups, one using the spray and one using an inactive spray. **Blind studies** offer another route to greater objectivity; they are studies in which neither the person administering the test nor the subjects involved know what is being tested or its expected effect. This way no one involved in the research can do anything to assist the outcome of the test or experiment.

The only way to develop critical faculties and improve the quality of your own research is to make a habit of reading journal articles. It is an important part of developing your sports science knowledge as well as your criticism skills. Remember that being critical means drawing out the strengths of the research as well as assessing its weaknesses.

Summary

This chapter has presented the basics of how to plan research and the range of considerations when embarking on a research project. It has also pointed out some of the problems that the researcher faces and the pitfalls that need to be avoided. Research is a central skill in any academic subject and needs to be embraced by a student to ensure that they perform well and open themselves up to the full experience of studying a subject. Completing a research project may seem daunting but if taken stage by stage it can be an experience that enhances the skills and the knowledge of the researcher. The researcher needs to show imagination, creativity, organization and management skills to complete a lengthy research project, and all these skills are desirable for the future when seeking employment.

Dig deeper

Online resources

Guide to undergraduate dissertations
www.socscidiss.bham.ac.uk/methodologies.html

National Foundation for Education Research
www.nfer.ac.uk/schools/developing-young-researchers/the-journey.cfm

Sport Psychology Research Methods
www.sportpsychologytoday.com/business-psychology/sport-psychology-research-methods-qualitative-vs-quantitative/

Sports Training Advisor
www.sports-training-adviser.com/research-methods.html

Books

A. Graham, *Statistics: A complete introduction* (London: Hodder Stoughton, 2014).

C. Gratton and I. Jones, *Research Methods for Sports Studies* (New York: Taylor and Francis, 2010).

C. Lynch, *Doing your Research Project in Sport* (Exeter: Learning Matters, 2010).

M. Smith, *Research Methods in Sport* (Exeter: Learning Matters, 2010).

J. Thatcher, R. Thatcher, M. Day, M. Portas and S. Hood, *Sport and Exercise Science* (Exeter: Learning Matters, 2009).

Fact-check

1 Which of the following statements about research is *false*?
  a The research hypothesis is what the researcher expects to find
  b The null hypothesis is the opposite of what the researcher expects to find
  c Variables are factors that may change
  d Researchers do not have to control variables

2 Which statement is the best definition of objectivity?
  a If the test were repeated, the same results would be produced
  b The test needs to be designed to ensure it is free from personal bias
  c The test needs to be designed to produce credible results
  d Does the test actually measure what you want it to test?

3 Which of the following statements describes qualitative research?
  a Statistical analyses are used to determine causal relationships
  b The researcher is aiming to produce results that are free from bias
  c Information is presented as opinions or viewpoints
  d Information is objective and can lack depth

4 Quantitative research relies heavily on which type of research method?
  a Laboratory-based tests
  b Interviews
  c Observations
  d Use of diaries

5 Which of the following measures of central tendency is the number in the middle of the data set?
  a Mean
  b Range
  c Median
  d Mode

6 What does standard deviation measure?
  a Normal distribution of data set
  b The shape of the distribution curve
  c The score most frequently occurring
  d Variation within a data set

7 Which of the following is an example of a paired t-test?
  a Mann-Whitney U
  b Wilcoxon
  c Bell curve
  d ANOVA

8 Which of the following is an example of an inferential statistic?
  a Correlation
  b Standard deviation
  c Range
  d Mean

9 What is the role of the abstract section of a journal article?

    a To introduce the article

    b To offer an alternative to reading the whole article

    c To provide a summary of the article

    d To provide the outcomes of the research

10 Which of the following information would *not* be present in a method?

    a Number of subjects

    b Profile of the researcher

    c Details of fees paid to subjects

    d Demographics of the subject

References

Introduction
BASES, *About BASES*: www.bases.org.uk/About (accessed 6 June 2015).

SkillsActive, *Sport*: www.skillsactive.com/sectors/sport (accessed 6 June 2015).

Chapter 2
Bursztyn, P.G., *Physiology for Sportspeople: A serious user's guide to the body* (Manchester: Manchester University Press, 1990).

Hamill, J. and Knutzen, K.M., *Biomechanical Basis of Human Movement*, 3rd edn (Baltimore, MD, MD: Lippincott, Williams & Wilkins, 2009).

Johnson, M.A., Polgar, J., Weightman, D. and Appleton, D., 'Data on the distribution of fibre types in thirty-six human muscles. An autopsy study', *Journal of the Neurological Sciences*, vol. 18, no.1 (1973), pp. 111–29.

McArdle, W.D., Katch, F.I. and Katch, V.L., *Exercise Physiology: Nutrition, energy, and human performance*, 7th edn (Baltimore, MD: Lippincott, Williams & Wilkins, 2010).

Nedergard, A., 'Muscles' in T. Rieger, F. Naclerio, A. Jiménez and J. Moody (eds), *EuropeActive's Foundations for Exercise Professionals* (Champaign, IL: Human Kinetics, 2015).

Tortora, G.J. and Derrickson, B., *Introduction to the Human Body: The essentials of anatomy and physiology*, 7th edn (New York: John Wiley, 2007).

Chapter 3
Bursztyn, P.G., *Physiology for Sportspeople: A serious user's guide to the body* (Manchester: Manchester University Press, 1990).

McArdle, W.D., Katch, F.I. and Katch, V.L., *Exercise Physiology: Nutrition, energy, and human performance*, 7th edn (Baltimore, MD: Lippincott, Williams & Wilkins, 2010).

Tortora, G.J. and Derrickson, B., *Introduction to the Human Body: The essentials of anatomy and physiology*, 7th edn (New York: John Wiley, 2007).

American Heart Association, *Understanding blood pressure readings*: www.heart.org/HEARTORG/Conditions/HighBloodPressure/AboutHighBloodPressure/Understanding-Blood-Pressure-Readings_UCM_301764_Article.jsp (accessed 17 March 2015).

Chapter 4
Adams, G.R., Harris, R.T., Woodard, D. and Dudley, G., 'Mapping of electrical muscle stimulation using MRI', *Journal of Applied Physiology*, vol.74 (1993), pp. 532–7.

Baechle, T.R. and Earle, R.W., *Essentials of Strength Training and Conditioning*, 3rd edn (Champaign, IL: Human Kinetics, 2008).

Campos, G.E.R., Luecke, T.J., Wendeln, H.K., Toma, K., Hagerman, F.C., Murray, T.F., Ragg, K.E., Ratamess, N.R., Kraemer, W.J. and Staron, R.S., 'Muscular adaptations in response to three different resistant-training regimens: Specificity of repetition maximum training zones', *European Journal of Applied Physiology*, vol. 88 (2002), pp. 50–60.

Chilibeck, P.D., Calder, A., Sale, D.G. and Webber, C.E., 'Twenty weeks of weight training increases lean tissue mass but not bone or mineral mass or density in healthy, active young women', *Canadian Journal of Physiological Pharmacology*, vol. 74 (1996), pp. 1180–5.

Goldspink, G., Schutt, A., Loughna, P.T., Wells, D.J., Jaenicke, T. and Gerlach, G.F., 'Gene expression in skeletal muscle in response to stretch and force generation', *American Journal of Physiology*, vol. 262 (1992), pp. 356–63.

Gollnick, P.D., 'Relationship of strength and endurance with metabolic potential', *International Journal of Sports Medicine*, vol. 3 (1982), pp. 26–32.

Hoffman, J., *Physiological Aspects of Sport Training and Performance* (Champaign, IL: Human Kinetics, 2014).

Lemon, W.R. and Nagle, F.J., 'Effects of exercise on protein and amino acid metabolism', *Medical Science Sports Exercise*, vol. 13 (1981), pp. 141–9.

McArdle, W.D., Katch, F.I. and Katch, V.L., *Exercise Physiology: Nutrition, energy, and human performance*, 7th edn (Baltimore, MD: Lippincott, Williams & Wilkins, 2010).

McCall, G.E., Byrnes, W.C., Dickinson, A. and Fleck, S.J., 'Muscle fibre hypertrophy, hyperplasia, and capillary density in college men after resistance training', *Journal of Applied Physiology*, vol. 81 (1996), pp. 2004–12.

MacDougall, J.D., Ward, G.R., Sale, D.G. and Sutton, J.R., 'Biochemical adaptation of human skeletal muscle to heavy resistance training and immobilization', *Journal of Applied Physiology*, vol. 43 (1977), pp. 700–3.

Minchna, H. and Hantman, G., 'Adaptation of tendon collagen to exercise', *International Orthopaedic*, vol. 13 (1989), pp. 161–5.

Ratamess, N., 'Adaptations to Anaerobic Training Programmes' in T.R. Baechle and R.W. Earle (eds), *Essentials of Strength Training and Conditioning*, 3rd edn (Champaign, IL: Human Kinetics, 2008).

Roman, W.J., Fleckenstein, J., Stray-Gundersen, J., Alway, S.E., Peshock, R. and Gonyea, W.J., *Journal of Applied Physiology*, vol. 74 (1993), no. 2, pp. 750–4.

Staron, R.S., Leonardi, M.J., Karapondo, D.L., Malicky, E.S., Falkel, J.E., Hagerman, F.C and Hikida, R.S., 'Strength and skeletal muscle adaptations in heavy resistance trained women after detraining and retraining', *Journal of Applied Physiology*, vol. 70 (1991), pp. 631–40.

West, D.W.D., Burd, N.A., Staples, A.W. and Phillips, S.M., 'Human exercise-mediated skeletal muscle hypertrophy is an intrinsic process', *International Journal of Biochemistry and Cell Biology*, vol. 42 (2010), pp. 1371–5.

Chapter 5

Anshel, M.H. and Sutarso, T., 'Conceptualising maladaptive sport perfectionism as a function of gender', *Journal of Clinical Sport Psychology*, vol. 4 (2010), pp. 263–81.

Arent, S.M. and Landers, D.M., 'Arousal, anxiety and performance: A re-examination of the Inverted U hypothesis', *Research Quarterly for Sport and Exercise*, vol. 74 (2003), pp. 436–44.

Atkinson, J.W., 'The mainstream of achievement oriented activity' in J.W. Atkinson and J.O. Raynor (eds), *Motivation and Achievement* (New York: Halstead, 1974).

Bandura, A., 'Self-efficacy: Toward a unifying theory of behavioural change', *Psychological Review*, vol. 84 (1977), pp. 191–215.

Bandura, A., *Social Foundations of Thoughts and Actions: A social cognitive theory* (Eaglewood Cliffs, NJ: Prentice Hall, 1986).

Bandura, A., *Self-efficacy: The exercise of control* (New York: Freeman, 1997).

Cox, R.H., *Sport Psychology: Concepts and applications*, 7th edn (New York: McGraw-Hill, 2012).

DeCharms, R.C., and Carpenter, V., 'Measuring motivation in culturally disadvantaged schoolchildren', *Journal of Experimental Education*, vol. 37 (1968), pp. 31–41.

Deci, E.L. and Ryan, R.M., *Intrinsic Motivation and Self-determination in Human Behavior* (New York: Plenum, 1985).

Deci, E.L., and Ryan, R.M., 'A motivational approach to self: Integration in personality', in R. Dienstbier (ed.), *Nebraska symposium on motivation*, vol. 38, *Perspectives on motivation*, pp. 237–88 (Lincoln, NE: University of Nebraska Press, 1991).

Deci, E.L., and Ryan, R.M., 'Self-determination theory and the facilitation of intrinsic motivation, social development, and wellbeing', *American Psychologist*, vol.55 (2000), pp. 68–78.

Dweck, C.S., *Mindset* (New York: Random House, 2006).

Easterbrook, J.A., 'The effect of emotion on cue utilization and the organization of behaviour', *Psychological Review*, vol. 66 (1959), pp. 183–201.

Fazey, J., and Hardy, L., *The Inverted U Hypothesis: A catastrophe for sport psychology?* British Association of Sports Sciences Monograph, no.1. NCF, Leeds, 1988).

Feltz, D.L., 'Self-efficacy as a cognitive mediator of athletic performance' in W.F. Straub and J.M. Williams (eds.), *Cognitive Sport Psychology* (Lansing, NY: Sport Science Associates, 1984).

Frett, G., 'York researcher finds that perfectionism can lead to imperfect health' (2004): http://yfile.news.yorku.ca/2004/06/02/york-researcher-finds-that-perfectionism-can-lead-to-imperfect-health/ (accessed 24 January 2015).

Hill, A.P., Hall, H.K. and Appleton, P.R., 'A comparative examination of the correlates of self-oriented perfectionism and conscientious achievement striving in male cricket academy players', *Psychology of Sport and Exercise*, vol. 4 (2010), pp. 162–8.

Huitt, W., *Motivation to Learn: An overview* (2001): www.edpsycinteractive.org/topics/motivation/motivate.html (accessed 27 November 2014).

Hull, C.L., *Principles of Behaviour* (New York: Appleton-Century-Crofts, 1943).

Jackson, B., Beauchamp, M. and Knapp, P., 'Relational efficacy beliefs in athlete dyads: An investigation using actor-partner interdependence models', *Journal of Sport and Exercise Psychology*, vol. 29 (2007), pp. 170–89.

Jacobsen, E., *Progressive Relaxation* (Chicago: University of Chicago Press, 1938).

Kerr, J.H., 'The experience of arousal: A new basis for studying arousal effects in sport', *Journal of Sport Sciences*, vol. 3 (1985), pp. 169–79.

Kerr, J.H., *Motivation and Emotion in Sport: Reversal theory* (Hove: Psychology Press, 1997).

Landers, D.M. and Arent, S.M., 'Arousal-Performance Relationships' in J.M. Williams (ed.), *Applied Sport Psychology: Personal growth to peak performance* (Boston, MA: McGraw-Hill, 2010), pp. 260–84.

Liu, D., Chen, X. and Yao, X., 'From autonomy to creativity: A multilevel investigation of the mediating role of harmonious passion', *Journal of Applied Psychology*, vol. 96 (2011), pp. 294–309.

Maehr, M.L. and Zusho, A., 'Achievement goal theory: The past, present and future' in K.R. Wentzel and A.Wigfield (eds), *Handbook of Motivation in School* (New York: Routledge, 2009), pp. 77–104.

Martens, R., *Sport Competitive Anxiety Test* (Champaign, IL: Human Kinetics, 1977).

Martens, R., Vealey, R.S. and Burton, D. (eds) (1990a), *Competitive Anxiety in Sport* (Champaign, IL: Human Kinetics, 1990).

Martens R., Burton, D. and Vealey, R.S. (1990b) 'Development and validation of Competitive State Anxiety Inventory-2 (CSAI-2)' in R. Martens, R.S. Vealey and D. Burton (eds) (1990a), *Competitive Anxiety in Sport* (Champaign, IL: Human Kinetics, 1990).

McClelland, D., *The Achieving Society* (New York: Free Press, 1961).

McMorris, T., *Acquisition and Performance of Sports Skills* (Chichester: John Wiley, 2004).

Morris, T. and Keohn, S., 'Self-confidence in sport and exercise' in T. Morris and J. Summers (eds), *Sport Psychology: Theory, applications and issues*, 2nd edn (Queensland, Australia: Wiley, 2004), pp. 175–209.

Mueller, C.M. and Dweck, C. S., 'Praise for intelligence can undermine children's motivation and performance', *Journal of Personality and Social Psychology*, vol. 75 (1998), no. 1, pp. 33–52.

Sage, G., *Introduction to Motor Behaviour: A neurophysiological approach*, 2nd edn (Reading, MA: Addison-Wesley, 1977).

Sage, G., *Motor Learning and Control* (Dubuque, IA: Brown, 1984).

Sager, S.S. and Stoeber J., 'Perfectionism, fear of failure and affective responses to success and failure: The central role of fear and experiencing fear and embarrassment', *Journal of Sport and Exercise Psychology*, vol. 11 (2009), pp. 177–87.

Selye, H., 'The stress concept: past, present and future' in C.L. Cooper (ed.), *Stress Research* (New York: John Wiley, 1983), pp. 1–20.

Smith, R.E., Smoll, F.L., Cumming, S.P. and Grossbard, J.R., 'Measurement of multidimensional sport performance anxiety in children and adults: The Sport Anxiety Scale-2, *Journal of Sport and Exercise Psychology*, vol. 28 (2006), pp. 479–501.

Stafford-Brown, J. and Rea, S., *BTEC National for Sport and Exercise Sciences*, 3rd edn (Abingdon: Hodder Arnold, 2010).

Stoeber, J., Otto, K., Pescheck, E., Becker, C. and Stoll, O, 'Perfectionism and competitive anxiety in athletes: Differentiating striving for perfection and negative reactions to imperfection, *Personality and Individual Differences*, vol. 42 (2007), pp. 959–69.

Tod, D., Thatcher, J. and Rahman, R., *Sport Psychology* (Basingstoke: Palgrave MacMillan, 2010).

Vallance, J.K.H., Dunn, J.G.H., and Dunn, J.L.C., 'Perfectionism, anger and situation criticality in competitive youth ice hockey', *Journal of Sport and Exercise Psychology*, vol. 28 (2006), pp. 383–406.

Vallerand, R.J. and Lozier, G.F., 'An integrative analysis of intrinsic and extrinsic motivation in sport', *Journal of Applied Sport Psychology*, vol. 11 (1999), pp. 142–69.

Vallerand, R. J., Blanchard, C. M., Mageau, G. A., Koestner, R., Ratelle, C. F., Leonard, M. et al., 'Les passions de lame: On obsessive and harmonious passion', *Journal of Personality and Social Psychology*, vol. 85 (2003), pp. 756–67.

Vallerand, R. J., Rousseau, F. L., Grouzet, F. M. E., Dumais, A., and Grenier, S., 'Passion in sport: A look at determinants and affective experiences', *Journal of Sport and Exercise Psychology*, vol. 28 (2006), pp. 455–78.

Weinberg, R.S. and Gould, D., *Foundations of Sport and Exercise Psychology*, 5th edn (Champaign, IL: Human Kinetics, 2015).

Wolpe, J., *Psychology by Reciprocal Inhibition* (Stanford, CA: Stanford University Press, 1958).

Yerkes, R.M. and Dodson, J.D., 'The relation of strength of stimulus to rapidity of habit formation', *Journal of Comparative Neurology of Psychology*, vol. 18 (1908), pp. 459–82.

Chapter 6

Burkett, B., *Sports Mechanics for Coaches*, 3rd edn (Champaign, IL: Human Kinetics, 2010).

Hay, J.G., *The Biomechanics of Sports Techniques*, 4th edn (Englewood Cliffs; NJ: Prentice-Hall, 1993).

Hall, S.J., *Basic Biomechanics*, 5th edn (New York: McGraw-Hill, 2007).

Hamilton, N., Weimar, W. and Luttgens, K., *Kinesiology: Scientific basis of human motion* (Boston, MA: McGraw-Hill, 2008).

Lee, J., 'Usain Bolt 10 meter splits, Fastest Top Speed, 2008 vs 2009' (2009): http://speedendurance.com/2009/08/19/usain-bolt-10-meter-splits-fastest-top-speed-2008-vs-2009/ (accessed 10 February 2015).

Serway, R.A. and Jewett, J.W., *Physics for Scientists and Teachers*, 9th edn (Boston, MA: Brooks/Cole, 2014).

Chapter 7

Bean, A., *The Complete Guide to Sports Nutrition*, 7th edn (London: Bloomsbury, 2013).

Bergstrom, J., Hermansen, L., Hultman, E. and Saltin, B., 'Diet, muscle glycogen, and physical performance', *Acta Physiologica Scandinavica*, vol. 71 (1967), pp. 140–50.

Burke, L., Angus, D.J., Cox, G.R., Cummings, N.K., Gawthorn, K. and Hargreaves, M., 'Effect of fat adaptation and carbohydrate restoration on metabolism and performance during prolonged cycling', *Journal of Applied Physiology*, vol. 89 (2000), pp. 2413–21.

Christiansen, E.H. and Hansen, O., 'Arbeitsfahigkeit und Ernahung', *Skandinavisches Archiv Fur Physiologie*, vol. 81 (1939), pp. 160–71.

Dill, D.B., 'Applied Physiology', *Annual Review of Physiology*, vol. 1 (1936), pp. 551–76.

Hargreaves, M., Hawley, J.A. and Jeukendrup, A., 'Pre-exercise carbohydrate and fat ingestion: Effects on metabolism and performance', *International Journal of Sport Nutrition*, vol. 22 (2004), pp. 21–38.

Howarth, K.R., Moreau, N.A., Phillips, S.M. and Gibala, M.J., 'Coingestion of protein with carbohydrate during recovery from endurance exercise stimulates skeletal muscle protein synthesis in humans', *Journal of Applied Physiology*, vol. 106 (2009), pp. 1394-1402.

Jeukendrup, A. and Gleeson, M., *Sports Nutrition: An introduction to energy production and performance*, 2nd edn (Champaign, IL: Human Kinetics, 2010).

Keys, A. (ed.), 'Coronary heart disease in seven countries', *Circulation*, vol.41 (1970), pp. 1–211.

Kreider, R.D., 'Protein' in B.I. Campbell and M.A. Spano (eds), *NSCA's Guide to Sport and Exercise Nutrition* (Champaign, IL: Human Kinetics, 2011).

Malhotra, A., 'Saturated fat is not the major issue', *British Medical Journal,* 347 (2013); f.6340.

Malhotra, A., Noakes, T. and Phinney, S., 'It is time to bust the myth of physical activity and obesity: you cannot outrun a bad diet, *British Journal of Sports Medicine* (2015): www.bjsm. bmj.com/content/early/2015/05/07/bjsports-2015-094911.full (accessed 24 April 2015).

McArdle, W.D., Katch, F.I. and Katch, V.L., *Sports and Exercise Nutrition*, 4th edn (Baltimore, MD: Lippincott, Williams & Wilkins, 2013).

Noakes, T., Volek, J.S. and Phinney, S.D., 'Low carbohydrate diets for athletes: what evidence?', *British Journal of Sports Medicine*, vol. 48, no. 14 (2014), pp. 1077–8.

Noakes, T., 'The dietary lies about heart disease', *Beginner Banting Course* (2015): http://portal.realmealrevolution.com/course_templates/view/1 (accessed 24 April 2015).

Phillips, S.M., and van Loon, L.J., 'Dietary protein for athletes: from requirements to optimum adaptation', *Journal of Sport Science*, vol. 29 (2011), supplement 1, pp. 29–38.

Schwartz, R.S., Kraus, S.M. and Schwartz, J.G., 'Study finds that long-term marathon participation in marathon training/racing is paradoxically associated with increased coronary plaque volume', *Missouri Medical* (2014), March/April.

Siri-Tarino, P.W., Sun, Q., Hu, F.B. and Krauss, R.M., 'Meta-analysis of prospective cohort studies evaluating the association of saturated fat with cardiovascular disease', *American Journal of Clinical Nutrition*, vol. 91 (2010), pp. 535–46.

Volek, J.S., Noakes, T. and Phinney, S.D., 'Rethinking fat as a fuel for endurance exercise', *European Journal of Sport Science*, vol.15 (2015), no. 1, pp. 13–20.

Webster, S., Rutt, R. and Weltman, A., 'Physiological effects of a weight loss regime practised by college wrestlers', *Medicine and Science in Exercise*, vol. 22 (1990), pp. 229–34.

Willett, W, C. and Ascherio, A., 'Trans fatty acids: are their effects marginal?', *American Journal of Public Health*, vol. 84 (1994), pp. 722–4.

Chapter 8

Ambridge, B., *Psy-Q* (London: Profile Books, 2014).

Burton, D. and Bartlett, S., *Practitioner Research for Teachers* (London: Paul Chapman, 2005).

Lynch, C., *Doing your Research Project in Sport* (Exeter: Learning Matters, 2010).

Miles, M.B. and Huberman, A.M., *Qualitative Data Analysis: An expanded sourcebook* (London: Sage, 1994).

Thatcher, J. and Day, M., 'Understanding research' in *Sport and Exercise Science*, J. Thatcher, R. Thatcher, M. Day, M. Portas and S. Hood, (Exeter: Learning Matters, 2009).

Fact-check answers

Chapter 2
1 b
2 d
3 b
4 a
5 c
6 d
7 c
8 a
9 d
10 b

Chapter 3
1 c
2 b
3 d
4 a
5 d
6 b
7 c
8 a
9 b
10 b

Chapter 4
1 a
2 b
3 a
4 d
5 c
6 a
7 b
8 c
9 b
10 c

Chapter 5
1 b
2 a
3 b
4 d
5 a
6 c
7 c
8 d
9 c
10 a

Chapter 6
1 b
2 d
3 b
4 a
5 b
6 d
7 b
8 a
9 b
10 c

Chapter 7
1 d
2 d
3 a
4 c
5 a
6 b
7 d
8 a
9 c
10 b

Chapter 8
1 d
2 b
3 c
4 a
5 c
6 d
7 b
8 a
9 c
10 b

Index

glycogen depletion 89
    increase in hydrogen ions 89
fats 166–70
    energy store 34
    and heart disease 169–70
    high-fat diets for athletes 175–6
    metabolism 77
    sources, function and energy yield 158
fatty acids 166–9
fibre (muscle) 22, 23–4, 25–8, 36
fibre (nutrition) 161, 162, 163
fixed versus growth mindset 96–8
fluid intake 172–3
food see nutrition
Fosbury flop technique 151
free radicals 171–2
frequency distribution curves 188
friction 146–9
fructose 160, 161, 163
fruit 171, 172, 174
fruit juices 161

gait 132
galactose 160
gaseous exchange in the lungs 47–8
glucose 34, 159–61
    breakdown of 35–6
glycaemic index (GI) 163–4
glycaemic load (GL) 164
glycogen 34
    breakdown of 35, 36, 76
    depletion of causing fatigue 89
    'glycogen sparing' 77
    levels following long-term training 75–6
    replacing depleted 174, 175
    storage of 160
Golgi tendon organs (GTOs) 31
gravity
    acceleration due to 133–4
    aiding venous return 63
    centre of 149–52
growth versus fixed mindset 96–8

harmonious passion 107
heart 52–8
    as a double-action pump 52–4
    blood vessels 55–6
    cardiac cycle 57–8
    cardiac output 57–8
    conduction system 57, 58
    valves 54–5
heart disease, link to saturated fat intake 169–70
heart rate 57, 58
    and cardiac hypertrophy 78
    and cardiac output 79
    increase in 72
    pulse measuring 61
high altitude, training at 82
high-carbohydrate diets 174–5
high-fat diets 175–6
high-intensity resistance training, and muscle size increases 84
high jump and the centre of mass 151
'hitting the wall' 77
hydration 172–3
hydrogen ions 89
hydrogenated vegetable oils 169
hyper-hydration 172
hyperplasia 85
hypertonic sports drinks 173
hypertrophy 84–5
    cardiac 78
hypo-hydration (dehydration) 172
hypotheses 181
hypotonic sports drinks 173

imagery 124–5
inertia, Newton's law of 134
inferential statistics 190
integumentary system 64
interviews 185
intrinsic motivation 103
inverted U hypothesis 112–15